Junior Anatomy Notebooking Journal

for

Exploring Creation with Human Anatomy and Physiology

by
Jeannie Fulbright

Junior Anatomy Notebooking Journal

Published by
Apologia Educational Ministries, Inc.
1106 Meridian Plaza, Suite 220/340
Anderson, IN 46016

www.apologia.com

Copyright © 2010 Jeannie Fulbright. All rights reserved.

Manufactured in the United States of America
Second Printing: March 2011

ISBN: 978-1-935495-47-5

Printed by Courier Printing, Kendallville, IN

Cover Design by Kim Williams

All Biblical quotations are from the New American Standard Bible, King James Version, New International Version or New King James Version
Cover photos licensed through Shutterstock
Sebastian Kaulitzki, Elena Kalistratova, Alexander Vasilyev, Artman, HKahn

Photo Credits

Illustrations by Kim Williams: Cover, 11
Illustrations by Rebecca Purifoy - 14, 15, 29, 30, 40, 41, 56, 57, 69, 70, 86, 87, 97, 98, 111, 112, 123, 124, 141, 142, 151, 152, 166, 167, 182, 183, 198, 199
Crestock: 99, 110, 114, 132 (top left), 161 (all), 225
Jupiter Images: 16, 18, 19, 27, 37, 38, 53, 54, 64, 65, 67, 68, 71, 73, 76, 77, 83, 84, 90, 91 (top right), 92, 93, 95, 96, 106. 107, 109, 118, 119, 121, 126 (bottom), 132 (neuron), 136, 137, 139, 143 (bottom), 146, 147, 149, 156, 157, 162 (top right), 164, 176, 177, 179, 184, 186, 187, 195, 196, 204, 205, 209, 220 (top right), 226
Shutterstock: 28, 39 (Matthew Cole), 42 (PeterG), 169 (Andrea Danti), 168 (Charobnica), 171 (Tootles), 180 (Charobnica)
Photos © 2007 Wolters Kluwer Health | Lippincott Williams and Wilkins: 31, 32, 33, 58, 59 (top) 60, 85, 106 (top), 91 (top left, both middle, bottom right), 113 (top), 122, 125, 132 (five images), 140, 143 (top), 145 (bottom two), 150, 153 (top right), 154, 162 (top right), 181, 185, 197, 201, 211 - 213, 216, 220, 226 (bottom two), 226 (left)
Wikimedia public domain: 59 (bottom), 126 (top), 144, 145 (top four), 153 (Attribution: Patrick J. Lynch top left)
Illustrations by Megan Fruchte: 89 (bottom), 91 (bottom left), 113 (bottom), 168 (top, bottom left), 220 (bottom left)
NEI.gov - 155

Fonts used with permission/license from:

Educational Fontware: AB Cursive, HWT
My Fonts.com: Ballerina -Paulo W., Intellecta Design, Ulma - Intellecta Designs, Paulo W., Treasury Gold - Canada Type, Otherworld - David F. Nalle - Scriptorium Font Library IntellectaBorders - Intellecta Designs, Paulo W., mariaBalleInitials - Fontographer, Geometr885 - Bitstream
Fontdiner.com: Fontdinerdotcom Jazz Light, Superstartlike
Various Designers: Puzzle Pieces - Font Environment, Futurex Apocalypse - www.cumberlandgames.com, CrayonAL - Maniackers Design, Baby Jeepers - Ray Laramie www.typodermic.com, Marker Felt - Pat Snyder, Endor - Graham Meade & Apostrophe, Acorn Initials - Typographer Mediengestaltung, Wedgie - David Rakowski, Powderfinger - Neumat Ick & Apostrophic Laboratories, McKloud - Jessica Slater & Apostrophic Labs, Merkin - Apostrophic Labs, Sins of Rhonda - Brain Eaters Font Co., Musicals - Brain Eaters

Note from the Author

Welcome to the wonderful adventure in learning called "Notebooking." This junior notebooking journal correlates with Apologia's *Exploring Creation with Human Anatomy and Physiology,* by Jeannie Fulbright and Brooke Ryan, M.D. It is designed for children that are not yet proficient writers. The activities in this journal provide everything your child needs to complete the assignments in *Exploring Creation with Human Anatomy and Physiology* and more. It will serve as your child's individual notebook. You only need to provide scissors, glue, colored pencils, a stapler and a few brass fasteners.

The concept of notebooking is not a new one. In fact, keeping notebooks was the primary way the learned men of our past educated themselves, from Leonardo Da Vinci and Christopher Columbus to George Washington, John Quincy Adams and Meriwether Lewis. These men and many others of their time were avid notebookers. As we know, they were also much more advanced in their knowledge—even as teens—than we are today. George Washington was a licensed surveyor during his teenage years, and John Quincy Adams graduated from law school at age 17.

It would be wise for us to emulate the methods of education of these great men, rather than the failing methods used in our schools today. Common modern methods, namely fill-in-the-blank and matching worksheets, do not fully engage the student's mind. Studies show that we remember only 5% of what we hear, 50% of what we see and hear and 90% of what we see, hear and do. When we participate in activities that correspond with learning, we increase our retention exponentially. This is exactly what the Junior Anatomy Notebooking Journal is designed to do—offer engaging learning activities to increase your student's retention.

The National Center for Educational Statistics shows us that American school children, by twelfth grade, rank at the bottom of international assessments, and do not even know 50% of what students in top-ranked countries know. As home educators, we have the opportunity to discard methods that are detrimental and ineffective and adopt the methods which will genuinely educate our children.

In addition to academic achievement, notebooking offers many benefits to students and parents. For students, it provides an opportunity to uniquely express themselves as they learn. It also provides a treasured memento of educational endeavors. For parents, it is a record of the year's studies and can easily be transferred to a portfolio if needed.

This journal will make notebooking easier for both you and your student by supplying a plethora of templates, hands-on crafts and projects, additional experiment ideas, and many activities that will engage your student in learning. It will prove invaluable in helping students create a wonderful keepsake of all they learned in human anatomy and physiology. Remember that *everything in this notebooking journal is optional.* Because it will serve as your student's own unique notebook, you may customize it by simply tearing out the activity pages that you choose not to use. You, as the teacher, will decide what truly benefits your student's learning experience, encourages a love for learning and builds his confidence in science. Every child is different, learns differently and will respond differently to the array of activities provided here. Use discernment in how many of the activities and assignments you use with your child. Your goal is not to complete every activity but to make learning a joy.

However, as a seasoned home educator, let me encourage you not to attempt to do every single activity in this notebooking journal. Choose the projects and activities that will be enjoyable and inspire a love of learning. If something is a drudgery, it will not serve to increase your student's retention, but will only discourage his enjoyment of science–resulting in an unmotivated learner.

It is my hope and prayer that you and your students will benefit from your studies this year, growing closer to God as you learn of His creation, and finding joy in the learning process.

Warmly,

Table of Contents

Table of Contents

Junior Anatomy Notebooking Journal

Below are descriptions of a suggested schedule and the activities included in this notebooking journal.

Suggested Schedule

A suggested schedule for reading the *Exploring Creation with Human Anatomy and Physiology* text and completing the activities contained in the book and in this journal has been provided. Please do not feel the need to complete every activity or assignment. Use the schedule as a guide, in a way that best suits your family.

Coloring Pages, Notebooking Assignments, Activities and Projects

Every lesson in this journal begins with coloring pages. Your student may wish to color these pages while the lesson is read aloud. Most lessons also include a template with several empty boxes and writing lines. After each reading session, encourage your child to use the boxes and lines to record information he found interesting in the reading. Your child can create illustrations, diagrams, or short narrations of what he's learned. By doing this, your child's retention of the material will be increased significantly. Following this template for creative expression is another template for completing the notebooking assignment from the text. Colored pencils are encouraged as they facilitate creativity and high quality work. Hands-on vocabulary activities are also provided for each lesson to help your student learn important anatomy terms.

Some experiments in the book require the student to use a Scientific Speculation Sheet. These sheets have been included in this notebooking journal. Drawings or pictures of the projects can be pasted onto the Scientific Speculation Sheets.

Scripture Copywork

Incorporating the Word of God in your science studies through Scripture Copywork will provide many benefits to your student. It will encourage stronger faith and memorization of Scripture, as well as better writing, spelling and grammar skills. The copywork is designed to be traced over and then recopied on the lines below the scriptures.

Project Pages

If your student chooses to do one of the projects in the book or one of the More to Explore suggestions, he may wish to include a drawing or photograph on the Project Page provided for that lesson. This will remind him of his project and what he learned. It will also serve as a record of his learning.

Cut and Fold Miniature Books

At the back of this journal, you will find Cut and Fold Miniature Book craft activities for each lesson. These are entirely optional. These miniature books are designed to review the concepts learned in each lesson. Paste Pages are included in this journal for each miniature book activity. The Paste Pages provide a place for your students to preserve and display their Cut and Fold Miniature Books. Instructions are included for cutting and assembling the miniature books.

More to Explore

The More to Explore suggestions are designed to give your student additional ideas and activities that might enhance his studies such as: experiments, hands-on activities, research and living book titles, as well as audio and video resources. Because these assignments are entirely optional, they are not included in the Suggested Schedule for completing the notebooking journal.

Field Trip Sheets

Your family may wish to further enhance your studies by visiting a science museum or perhaps the Bodies Exhibit. Field Trip Sheets are provided at the back of this notebooking journal to record your visits. You can make a pocket on the back of these sheets to hold any brochures or additional information you receive. Simply glue three edges (sides and bottom) of a half piece of construction paper to the bottom of the Field Trip Sheet.

Week	Day 1	Day 2
1	**Lesson 1 - Introduction to Human Anatomy & Physiology** Read *T pp. 19-22* & Narrate Begin working on Coloring Pages about the History of Anatomy *NJ pp. 14-15* Try This! *T p. 21* Read *T pp. 22-24* & Narrate Try This! *T p. 23*	Read *T pp. 24-26* & Narrate Try This! *T p. 26* Read *T pp. 26-28* & Narrate Begin recording facts about *Anatomy and Physiology NJ p. 16* Drawing: Cell Anatomy *T p. 26, NJ p. 17*
2	**Lesson 1 - Introduction to Human Anatomy & Physiology** Read *T pp. 29-31* & Narrate Read *T pp. 31-33* & Narrate Notebooking Activity: History of Anatomy *T p. 33, NJ pp. 18-19*	Personal Person Project: Create Personal Person *T p. 33, NJ p. 13* Scripture Copywork *NJ pp. 20-21* Vocabulary Lift the Flap *NJ pp. 23* Cell Minibook *NJ Appendix. p. A 7* Project: Edible Cell *T p. 35, NJ p. 28*
3	**Lesson 2 - The Skeletal System** Read *T pp. 37-40* & Narrate Begin working on Coloring Pages about the Skeletal System *NJ p. 29-30* Try This! *T p. 37* Try This! *T p. 38* Read *T pp. 41-42* & Narrate	Read *T pp. 42-44* & Narrate Try This! *T p. 43* Begin recording facts about the *Skeletal System NJ p. 31* Read *T pp. 45-48* & Narrate Read *T pp. 49-50* & Narrate Try This! *T p. 49* Try This! *T p. 50*
4	**Lesson 2 - The Skeletal System** Read *T pp. 51-52* & Narrate Try This! *T p. 51* Notebooking Activity: Label a Skeleton *T p. 52, NJ p. 32*	Personal Person Project: Add some bones *T p. 52 NJ p. 13* Anatomy Identification *NJ pp. 33* Scripture Copywork *NJ pp. 34-35* Bones Minibook *NJ Appendix p. A 11* Experiment: Analyzing a Chicken Bone *T p. 53, NJ p. 39*
5	**Lesson 3 - The Muscular System** Read *T pp. 55-57* & Narrate Try This! *T p. 56* Begin working on Coloring Pages about the Muscular System *NJ pp. 40-41* Read *T pp. 57-60* & Narrate Try This! *T p. 58*	Try This! *T p. 61* Begin recording information about the Muscular System *NJ p. 42* Read *T pp. 61-64* & Narrate Try This! *T p. 62* Try This! *T p. 63*
6	**Lesson 3 - The Muscular System** Read *T pp. 64-66* & Narrate Try This! *T p. 66* Personal Person Project: Add some muscles *T p. 67, NJ p. 15*	Notebooking Activity: The Muscle Times *T p. 67, NJ p. 43* Vocabulary Puzzle Game *NJ pp. 45-49* Scripture Copywork *NJ pp. 50-51* Muscles Minibook *NJ Appendix p. A 13* Experiment: Growing Muscle *T p. 67, NJ p. 55*
7	**Lesson 4 - The Digestive & Renal Systems** Read *T pp. 69-71* & Narrate Begin working on Coloring Pages about the Digestive and Renal Systems *NJ pp. 56-57* Try This! *T p. 71* Read *T pp. 71-73* & Narrate Try This! *T p. 72*	Read *T pp. 74-77* & Narrate Begin recording facts about and labeling the Digestive System *NJ p. 58-60* Try This! *T p. 76* Read *T pp. 77-80* & Narrate Try This! *T p. 78*
8	**Lesson 4 - The Digestive and Renal Systems** Read *T pp. 80-81* & Narrate Notebooking Activity: Digestion Comic Strip *T p. 81, NJ p. 61*	Personal Person Project: Add the digestive and renal systems *T p. 82, NJ p. 13* Vocabulary Crosswords *NJ pp. 62-63* Scripture Copywork *NJ pp. 64-65* Digestion Minibook *NJ Appemdix. p. A 15* Project: Design a Digestion Theme Park *T p. 82, NJ p. 68*

*Page numbers for the anatomy text are indicated by *T p.* Page numbers for the notebooking journal are indicated by *NJ p.*

Week	Day 1	Day 2
9	**Lesson 5 - Health and Nutrition** Read *T pp. 85-88* & Narrate Begin working on Coloring Pages about Health and Nutrition *NJ p. 69-70* Try This! *T p. 87* Read *T pp. 88-89* & Narrate Try This! *T p. 89*	Read *T pp. 90-92* & Narrate Begin recording facts about Health and Nutrition *NJ p. 71* Try This! *T p. 91* Try This! *T p. 92* Read *T pp. 93-95* & Narrate Try This! *T p. 93* Try This! *T p. 96*
10	**Lesson 5 - Health and Nutrition** Read *T pp. 96-98* & Narrate Project: Food Pyramid *T p. 99, NJ p. 72* Notebooking Activity: One-Week Dinner Menu *T p. 98, NJ p. 73-75*	Scripture Copywork *NJ pp. 76-77* Vocabulary Lift the Flap *NJ pp. 79-81* Nutrition Minibook *NJ Appendix p. A 21* Experiment: Testing for Vitamin C *T p. 99, NJ p. 85*
11	**Lesson 6 - The Respiratory System** Read *T pp. 103-106* & Narrate Begin working on Coloring Pages About the Respiratory System *NJ pp. 86-87* Try This! *T p. 104* Try This! *T p. 105*	Read *T pp. 106-110* & Narrate Begin recording facts about the Respiratory System *NJ p. 88* Try This! *T p. 106* Try This! *T p. 108* Try This! *T p. 109* Try This! *T p. 110*
12	**Lesson 6 - The Respiratory System** Read *T pp. 111-115* & Narrate Try This! *T p. 114* Try This! *T p. 115* Label the Respiratory System *NJ p. 89* Personal Person Project: Add a trachea, lungs and diaphragm *T p. 116, NJ p. 13*	Notebooking Activity: Write a Speech: The Dangers of Smoking *T p. 116, NJ p. 90* Anatomy Identification *NJ p. 91* Scripture Copywork *NJ pp. 92-93* Respiratory Minibooks *NJ Appendix p. A 25* Experiment: Diaphragm Model *T p. 116* Experiment: Vital Lung Capacity *T p. 117*
13	**Lesson 7 - Life in the Blood** Read *T pp. 119-122* & Narrate Begin working on Coloring Pages about Blood *NJ pp. 97-98* Try This! *T p. 122*	Read *T pp. 123-126* & Narrate Project: Blood Model *T p. 124* Try This! *T p. 127*
14	**Lesson 7 - Life in the Blood** Read *T pp. 127-131* & Narrate Notebooking Activity: Blood Illustration *T p. 131, NJ p. 99*	Notebooking Activity: Write an Apologia *T p. 131, NJ p. 100* Vocabulary Puzzle Game *NJ pp. 101-105* Scripture Copywork *NJ pp. 106-107* Blood Minibooks *NJ Appendix p. A 29* Experiment: Type Your Blood *T p. 132*
15	**Lesson 8 - The Cardiovascular System** Read *T pp. 133-135* & Narrate Begin working on Coloring Pages about the Cardiovascular System *NJ pp. 111-112* Try This! *T p. 135* Read *T pp. 136-138* & Narrate Try This! *T p. 136* Try This! *T p. 137*	Read *T pp. 139-141* & Narrate Try This! *T p. 139* Begin recording facts about the Cardiovascular System and label the heart *NJ p. 113* Try This! How Blood Flows Through the Heart *T p. 141* Read *T pp. 142-144* & Narrate Try This! *T p. 143*
16	**Lesson 8 - The Cardiovascular System** Read *T pp. 144-145* & Narrate Notebooking Activity: Write an Advertisement *T p. 146, NJ p. 114*	Personal Person Project: Add a heart *T p. 146, NJ p. 13* Vocabulary Lift the Flap *NJ pp. 115-117* Scripture Copywork *NJ pp. 118-119* Cardiovascular Minibooks *NJ Appendix p. A 33* Project: Make a Stethoscope *T p. 147, NJ p. 122*

*Page numbers for the anatomy text are indicated by *T p.* Page numbers for the notebooking journal are indicated by *NJ p.*

Week	Day 1	Day 2
17	**Lesson 9 - The Nervous and Endocrine Systems** Read *T pp. 149-152* & Narrate Begin working on Coloring Pages about the Nervous and Endocrine Systems *NJ pp. 123-124* Try This! *T p. 151*	Read *T pp. 152-155* & Narrate Try This! *T p. 154* Begin recording facts about the Nervous and Endocrine Systems *NJ p. 125* Read *T pp. 155-157* & Narrate Try This! *T pp. 156* Try This! *T pp. 157*
18	**Lesson 9 - The Nervous and Endocrine Systems** Read *T pp. 158-159* & Narrate Personal Person Project: Add a brain *T p. 159, NJ p. 13* Notebooking Activities: Label a Brain and Neuron, Make a Venn Diagram *T p. 159, NJ pp. 126-127*	Nervous System Hangers *NJ pp. 129-135* Scripture Copywork *NJ pp. 136-137* Nervous System Minibook *NJ Appendix p. A 37* Project: Anatomy Trivia Game *T p. 160, NJ p. 140*
19	**Lesson 10 - The Nervous System Extended** Read *T pp. 161-164* & Narrate Begin working on Coloring Pages about the Nervous System Extended *NJ p. 141-142* Try This! *T p. 162* Begin recording facts about the Nervous System *NJ p. 143* Try This! *T p. 164*	Read *T pp. 165-167* & Narrate Try This! *T p. 165* Try This! *T p. 166* Try This! *T p. 167* Read *T pp. 167-169* & Narrate Try This! *T p. 168*
20	**Lesson 10 - The Nervous System Extended** Read *T pp. 170-171* & Narrate Try This! *T p. 170* Notebooking Activity: The Cerebral Lobes *T p. 172, NJ p. 144*	Anatomy Identification *NJ p. 145* Scripture Copywork *NJ pp. 146-147* Brain Minibook *NJ Appendix p. A 41* Project: Design a Science Fair Project *T p. 172, NJ p. 150*
21	**Lesson 11 - Your Senses** Read T pp. 175-177 & Narrate Begin working on Coloring Pages about Your Senses *NJ pp. 151-152* Try This! *T p. 176* Try This! *T p. 177* Try This! *T p. 178* Read *T pp. 178-181* & Narrate Try This! *T p. 179* Try This! *T p. 180* Try This! *T p. 181*	Read T pp. 182-185 & Narrate Try This! *T p. 182* Try This! *T p. 183* Try This! *T p. 185* Begin recording facts about the Your Senses *NJ p. 153-154* Read *T pp. 186-188* & Narrate Try This! *T p. 186* Try This! *T p. 187* Try This! *T p. 188*
22	**Lesson 11 - Your Senses** Read *T pp. 189-191* & Narrate Try This! *T p. 189* Try This! *T p. 190* Notebooking Activity: Diagram of the Eye *T p. 191, NJ p. 155*	Scripture Copywork *NJ pp. 156-157* Anatomy Match Up *NJ pp. 159-162* Senses Minibook *NJ Appendix p. A 43* Experiment: Testing Taste *T p. 192*
23	**Lesson 12 - The Integumentary System** Read *T pp. 195-198* & Narrate Begin working on Coloring Pages about the Integumentary System *NJ pp. 166-167* Read *T pp. 198-201* & Narrate Try This! *T p. 200* Begin recording facts about Your Skin *NJ p. 168*	Read *T pp. 202-204* & Narrate Try This! *T p. 202* Try This! *T p. 203* Try This! *T p. 204* Read *T pp. 205-207* & Narrate Try This! *T p. 206* Try This! *T p. 207*

*Page numbers for the anatomy text are indicated by *T p*. Page numbers for the notebooking journal are indicated by *NJ p*.

Week	Day 1	Day 2
24	**Lesson 12 - The Integumentary System** Read *T pp. 208-209* & Narrate Try This! *T p. 208* Personal Person Project: Add the skin *T p. 209, NJ p. 13* Notebooking Activity: Diagram of Skin *T p. 209, NJ p. 169*	Notebooking Activity: Fingerprints *T p. 209, NJ p. 170* Project: Braille Challenge *T p. 211, NJ p. 171* Vocabulary Lift the Flap *NJ pp. 173-175* Scripture Copywork *NJ pp. 176-177* Integumentary Minibook *NJ Appendix p. A 49* Experiment: Sensing Sensitivity *T p. 212, NJ p. 181*
25	**Lesson 13 - The Lymphatic and Immune Systems** Read *T pp. 215-218* & Narrate Begin working on Coloring Pages about the Lymphatic and Immune Systems *NJ pp. 182-183* Read *T pp. 219-221* & Narrate	Read *T pp. 221-224* & Narrate Read *T pp. 224-227* & Narrate
26	**Lesson 13 - The Lymphatic and Immune Systems** Notebooking Activity: The Body's Defenses *T p. 227, NJ pp. 184-185*	Scripture Copywork *NJ pp. 186-187* Vocabulary Puzzle Game *NJ pp. 189-193* Defense Minibook *NJ Appendix p. A 53* Experiment: Testing for Bacteria and Fungi *T p. 228, NJ p. 197*
27	**Lesson 14 - Growth and Development** Read *T pp. 231-235* & Narrate Begin working on Coloring Pages about Growth and Development and Human Beings *NJ pp. 198-199* Try This! *T p. 233* Read *T pp. 235-238* & Narrate Try This! *T p. 236*	Read *T pp. 238-241* & Narrate Try This! *T p. 242* Begin working on facts about Growth and Development *NJ p. 200* Read *T pp. 242-245* & Narrate Record whatever you'd like on the God Created Me page *NJ p. 201*
28	**Lesson 14 - Growth and Development** Read *T pp. 245-248* & Narrate Notebooking Activity: Stages of Development *T p. 248, NJ p. 202* Notebooking Activity: Possible Purpose Page *T p. 248, NJ p. 203* Prayer Journal Activity *T p. 248*	Bible Reading Plan *T p. 249* Scripture Copywork *NJ pp. 204-205* Vocabulary Crossword *NJ pp. 206-207* Growth and Development Minibook *NJ Appendix p. A 55* Project: Dominant and Recessive Traits *T p. 250, NJ p. 210*

*Page numbers for the anatomy text are indicated by **T p.** Page numbers for the notebooking journal are indicated by **NJ p.**

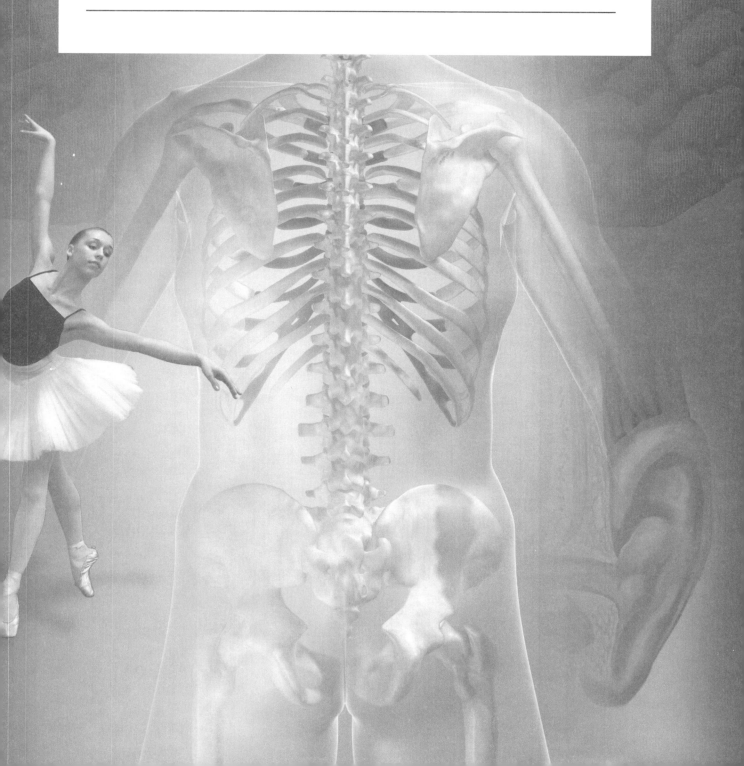

This journal belongs to:

_____

PERSONAL

PERSONAL

PERSON

PERSON

The instructions for creating your Personal Person can be found on page 12 of your anatomy textbook. The templates can be found in the appendix of this notebooking journal.

I am the LORD your God who brought you out from the land of Egypt to be your God; I am the LORD your God.

Numbers 15:41

But you have been washed and made holy, and you have received God's approval in the name of the Lord Jesus Christ and in the Spirit of our God.   I Corinthians 6:11

Anatomy and Physiology
Lesson 1

Cell Anatomy
Lesson 1

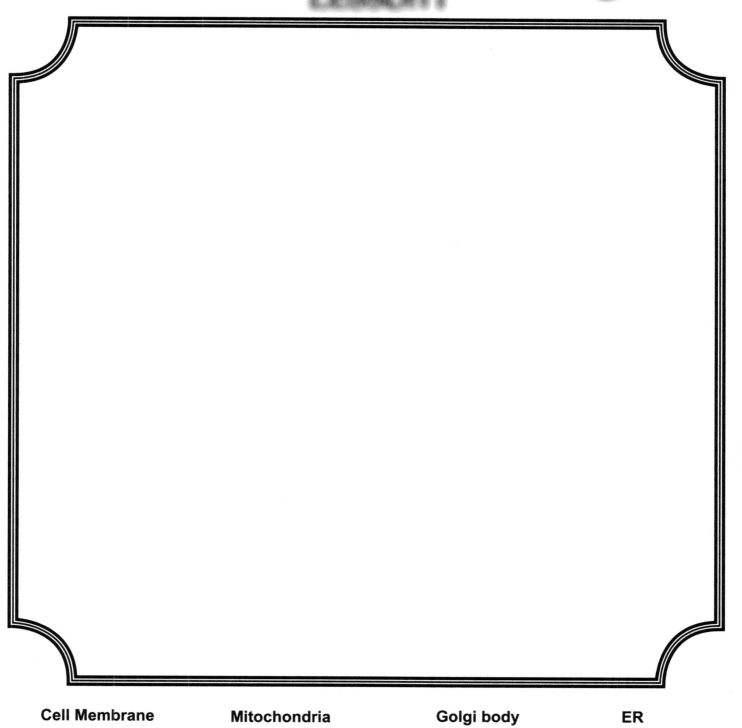

Cell Membrane   **Mitochondria**   **Golgi body**   **ER**

Ribosomes   **Centrioles**   **Lysosomes**   **Nucleus**

Egyptians

Hebrews

Greeks

Romans

Europeans

Microscope

Copywork

I will give thanks to You,
for I am fearfully and
wonderfully made.

Psalm 139:14

Copywork

I will give thanks to You, for I am fearfully and wonderfully made.

Psalm 139:14

VOCABULARY LIFT THE FLAP
LESSON 1

Tear out this page. Cut out each word and match it to the correct definition on the following page. Then, place glue along the top edge of the back of each word and glue above the line on each definition. Once the glue is dry, fold back the word to reveal the definition.

CYTOPLASM	NUCLEUS
ANATOMY	PHYSIOLOGY
CELL MEMBRANE	MITOCHONDRIA
HYPOTHESIS	LYSOSOMES

ANATOMY VOCABULARY
LESSON 1

Glue correct word above this line, then fold back.

The study of the human body, all its parts, and how it's put together.

Glue correct word above this line, then fold back.

An educated guess.

Glue correct word above this line, then fold back.

The wall around a cell.

Glue correct word above this line, then fold back.

The control center of the cell.

Glue correct word above this line, then fold back.

The study of how all the parts of the body function.

Glue correct word above this line, then fold back.

The jelly-like substance inside a cell, in which all the organelles float.

Glue correct word above this line, then fold back.

Organelles that protect the cell from foreign invaders and break down chemicals.

Glue correct word above this line, then fold back.

The organelles inside the cell that give the cell power.

Cell Minibook
Lesson 1

Paste your Cell Wheel
onto this page.

Be a Modern Vesalius

Vesalius drew the human body quite accurately. Using images found on page 32 of your textbook, try to draw the internal organs of a human body to scale. Also, Vesalius built prosthetics that are still used as models today. Using different materials attempt to build a prosthetic leg or arm that bends with the use of a pulley and strings. You can use materials such as: funnels, cardboard tubes, strings, metal fasteners, plastic rings, cardboard, tape and glue.

Experiment with a Magnifying Glass or Microscope

It's fascinating to view things up close. Use a magnifying glass or microscope to get a better look at your anatomy! Try looking at your skin, hair, fingernails, teeth, eyes, or nose. It would also be interesting to see a scab or open wound up close. Another idea is to get a closer look at different foods or vitamins. Are you surprised at what you see?

Build a Microscope

There are many Internet sites that give instructions for building a simple to complex microscope. Do a search for instructions and attempt to build your own scope!

Book Suggestions

The History of Medicine by John Hudson Tiner. This is a wonderful, well written book on the history of anatomy. It's a must read for everyone and is sure to become a family favorite!

Enjoy Your Cells by Fran Balkwill & Mic Rolph. This book does a great job of teaching about cells, though it does not cover the specific functions of the organelles within the cells. That will be covered well in the first lesson of *Exploring Creation with Human Anatomy and Physiology*.

Galen and the Gateway to Medicine by Jeanne Bendick. This fascinating biography brings Galen's Roman world alive! It helps the reader understand the medical knowledge and practices of that time period. The maps, diagrams and charts are helpful additions to the text. Recommended for ages 10 and up.

DVD Suggestions

Magic School Bus: The Human Body. This DVD explores the human body. You may need to remind your children that lying is wrong as one child continually lies in the video.

Cell-a-bration Cytology: Newton's Workshop. Learn about cells with this live action DVD as Grandpa Newton and the kids explore God's creation with an old microscope. (Ages 7-12) 60 minutes.

DNA Decoders: Newton's Workshop. Learn about DNA with this live action DVD. (Ages 7-12) 60 minutes.

My Anatomy Projects
Lesson 1

What I did:

What I did:

What I learned:

What I learned:

Do not be wise in your own eyes; fear the
LORD and shun evil.   Proverbs 3:7

This will bring health to your body and
nourishment to your bones.   Proverbs 3:8

THE SKELETAL SYSTEM
LESSON 1

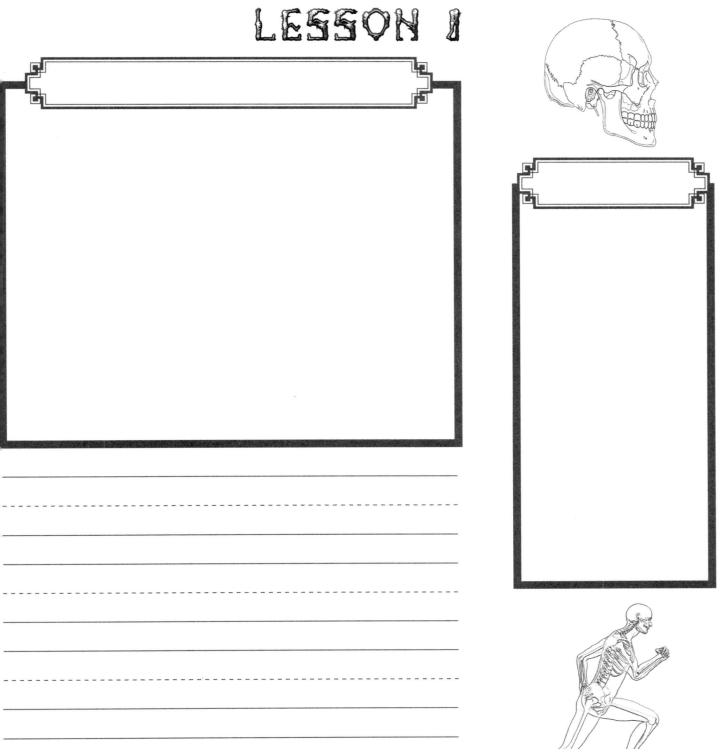

SKELETON
LESSON 1

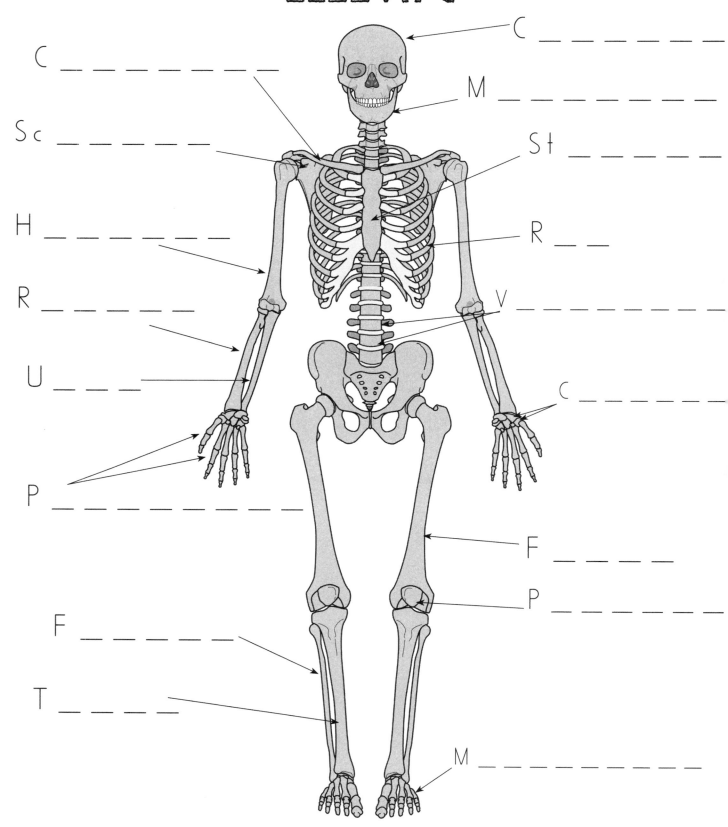

C _ _ _ _ _ _ _

M _ _ _ _ _ _ _ _

C _ _ _ _ _ _

Sc _ _ _ _ _ _ _

St _ _ _ _ _ _

H _ _ _ _ _ _ _

R _ _

R _ _ _ _ _ _ _

V _ _ _ _ _ _ _ _ _

U _ _ _ _

C _ _ _ _ _ _ _

P _ _ _ _ _ _ _ _ _ _

F _ _ _ _ _

P _ _ _ _ _ _ _

F _ _ _ _ _ _ _

T _ _ _ _ _

M _ _ _ _ _ _ _ _ _ _

32

Anatomy Identification

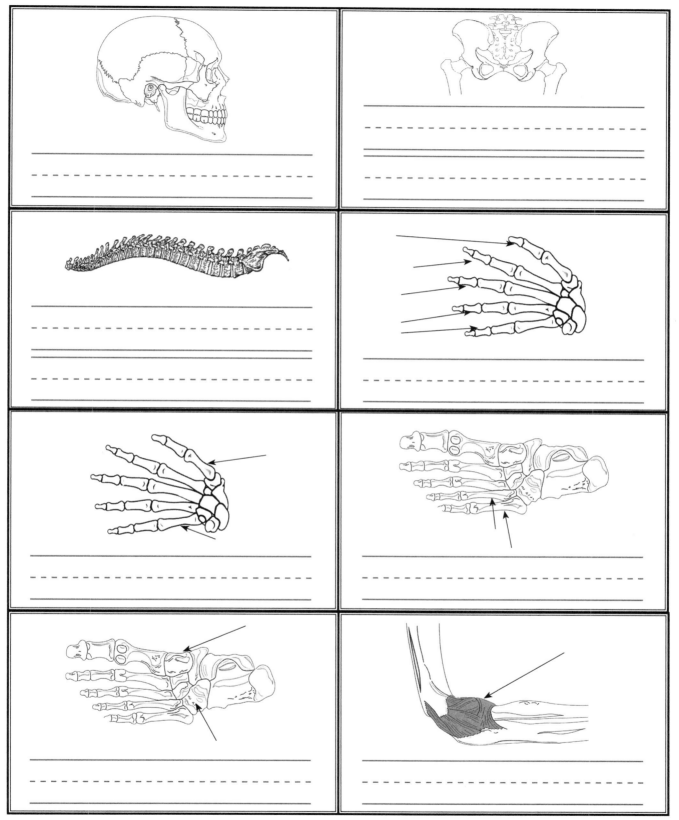

Write the correct names under the pictures.

Skull   Vertebral Column   Metacarpals   Tarsals

Metatarsals   Pelvic Girdle   Ligaments   Phalanges

Copywork

And the LORD will ... give
strength to your bones.
Isaiah 58: 11

Copywork

And the LORD will...give strength to your bones.

Isaiah 58:11

BONES MINIBOOK
LESSON I

Paste your Skeletal System
Shutter Book onto this page.

Do a Word Study

What does the Bible say about bones? Use a concordance to find out! Look up the words "bone" and "bones" to see all the verses that contain these two words. Do a word study by looking up the verses. Write down your findings and present what the Bible says about bones to your family.

Reconstruct a Skeleton

Find a large picture of a skeleton and study the locations of the bones. Cut out each bone from the skeleton, then see if you can reconstruct the skeleton without looking at a model.

Test the Bone Strength of Different Animals

Over the course of a few weeks, save any bones from the different meals your family eats. Try to get an assortment of bones from different kinds of animals: cows, chickens, pigs and fish.

Now make a guess about which animal you think has the strongest bones. Test all the bones by submerging them in vinegar to find out which ones break down the quickest. Check the bones every day for two weeks, noting which ones are soft and pliable. Which animal's bones remained strong and sturdy? Was your original guess correct?

Examine X rays

X rays were discovered because of how radiation changed photo paper. Do some fun experiments with photosensitive paper. You can either get a Photo Print Kit (I saw some on eBay) or buy some paper from a supplier. Alternately, you can make photosensitive paper yourself using ferric ammonium citrate (be sure to discard it properly as it can contaminate the environment).

Bones for Dinner?

Did you know that bones are full of nutrition? It's true! People used to eat bone marrow for its nutritional value. It was even considered a delicacy! Chicken bones were also used in soups because of the minerals they provide. You can do an Internet search to find other ways in which people enjoyed the nutritional value of bones! Yum!

Book Suggestion

Roentgen: The Head Bone's Connected to the Neck Bone by McClafferty. I personally read and enjoyed this book.

DVD Suggestion

Standard Deviants School - Anatomy, Program 1 - Bones (Classroom Edition). This fast paced, action packed DVD takes you on an exciting journey into the skeletal system.

My Bones Projects
Lesson 2

What I did:

What I did:

What I learned:

What I learned:

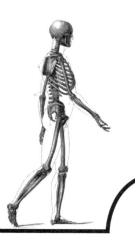

SCIENTIFIC SPECULATION SHEET

Analyzing a Chicken Bone

Lesson 2

Name_____ Date _____

Materials Used:

Procedure:

Hypothesis:

Results:

Conclusion:

The Lord GOD is my strength,
And He has made my feet like hinds' feet,

And makes me walk on my high places.

Habakkuk 3:19

The Muscular System
Lesson 3

MUSCLE TIMES

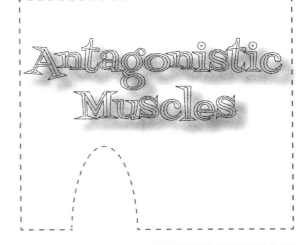

The muscles that are attached to your bones.

These muscles do not have stripes (striations) and are found in blood vessels, the stomach, the intestines and the bladder.

These connect skeletal muscles to the bones.

Cut out each puzzle piece on this page and the next. Match each vocabulary word puzzle piece to the correct definition puzzle piece. Cut out this rectangle and glue it to your Puzzle Page along the bottom and side edges to create a pocket. After you've played your Vocabulary Puzzle Game a few times, place all your puzzle pieces in the pocket for safe keeping.

Glue along this edge

Glue along this edge

Glue along this edge

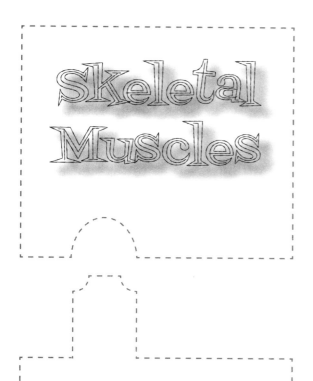

Skeletal Muscles

A condition that occurs when
a muscle is underused and
therefore becomes weak
and shrinks.

Tendons

A pair of muscle groups that
pulls the bone in opposite
directions.

This is another name for
skeletal muscles, because
you can control them by
thinking about controlling
them.

Smooth Muscles

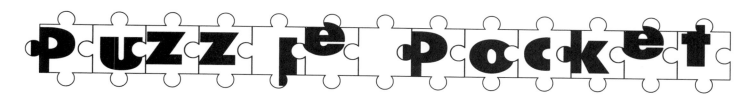

Paste your puzzle pocket here.

The LORD is my strength
and my song; he has
become my salvation.

Exodus 15:2

Copywork

The LORD is my strength and my song; he has become my salvation.

Exodus 15:2

Paste your Muscular
System Flap Book onto
this page.

Bible Study on Strength

Our muscles give us strength. What does the Bible say about strength? Use a concordance to find out! Look up the word "strength" to see all the verses that contain this word. Do a word study by looking up the verses. Write down your findings. Also, write down any area in which you feel you need God's strength, then ask God to strengthen you in this area. Encourage your family by presenting what the Bible says about strength.

Book Suggestion

Muscles: Our Muscular System by Seymour Simons. This book is highly ranked and contains beautiful illustrations and great content concerning the different muscle groups. Be aware that it may contain teachings on evolution.

DVD Suggestion

Human Body: Pushing the Limits Disc 1. Although overly focused on evolution, this DVD on muscle strength and the amazing design and abilities of the human body is extremely well done. If you choose to watch this DVD, keep in mind that there is no evidence for evolution. Rather, it is our great God who designed the intricacies of the human body.

My Muscles Projects
Lesson 3

What I did:

What I did:

What I learned:

What I learned:

SCIENTIFIC SPECULATION SHEET

Growing Muscle

Lesson 3

Name_____   Date _____

Materials Used:

Procedure:

Hypothesis:

Results:

Conclusion:

But solid food is for the mature, who by constant use have trained themselves to distinguish good from evil.
Hebrews 5:14

How sweet are Your words to my taste! Yes, sweeter than honey to my mouth!

Psalm 119:103

The DIGESTIVE SYSTEM
Lesson 4

The DIGESTIVE SYSTEM
Lesson 4

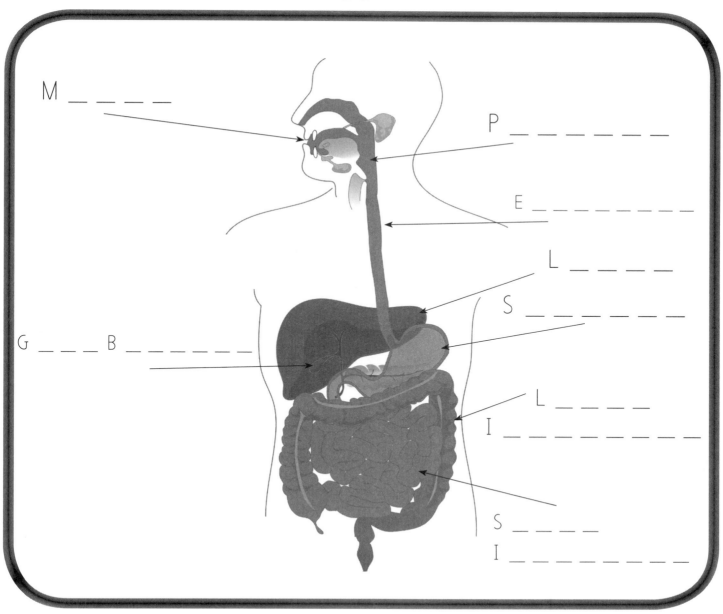

M _ _ _ _ _

P _ _ _ _ _ _ _

E _ _ _ _ _ _ _ _

L _ _ _ _ _

S _ _ _ _ _ _ _

G _ _ _ _ B _ _ _ _ _ _ _ _

L _ _ _ _ _

I _ _ _ _ _ _ _ _

S _ _ _ _ _

I _ _ _ _ _ _ _ _

The DIGESTIVE SYSTEM
Lesson 4

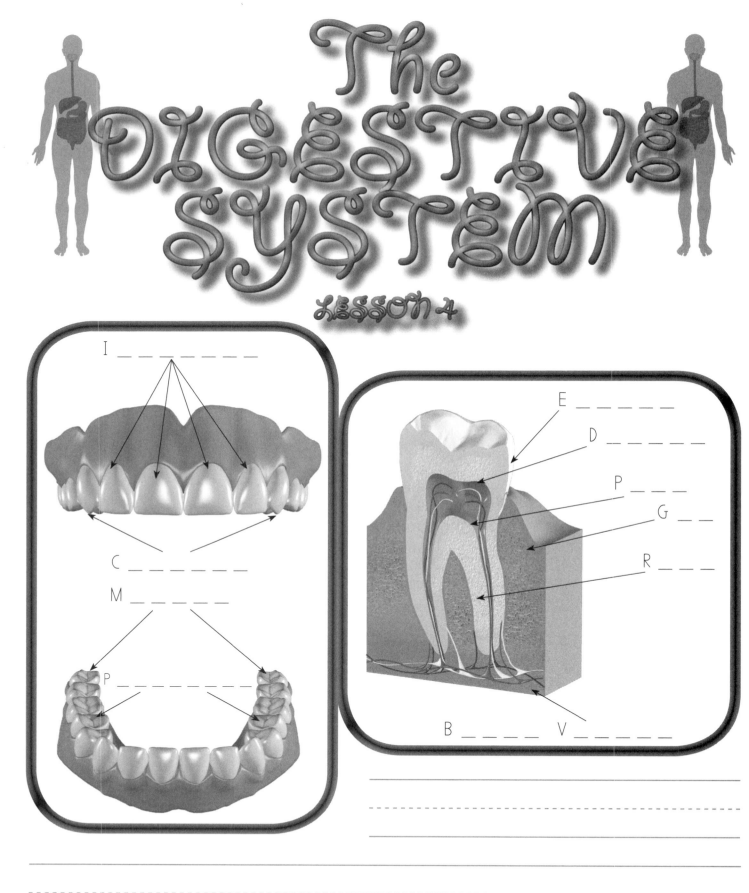

I _ _ _ _ _ _ _ _

C _ _ _ _ _ _ _ _

M _ _ _ _ _ _

P _ _ _ _ _ _ _ _

E _ _ _ _ _ _

D _ _ _ _ _ _ _

P _ _ _ _

G _ _ _

R _ _ _ _

B _ _ _ _ _ _   V _ _ _ _ _ _ _ _

Digestion Comic

DIGESTION CROSSWORD
LESSON 4

KIDNEYS

SMALL INTESTINE

ENAMEL

ENZYMES

CHEMICAL DIGESTION

MECHANICAL DIGESTION

ALIMENTARY CANAL

EPIGLOTTIS

LARGE INTESTINE

DENTIN

DIGESTION CROSSWORD
LESSON 4

Across

6. The living substance under the enamel on your tooth that supports it and absorbs shock that could otherwise damage the tooth.
7. The part of digestion where chemicals in foods are changed into smaller chemicals so your body can absorb and use them.
9. The special organs in your renal system that make urine.
10. The longest part of the digestive tract where most of the chemical digestion occurs and food is absorbed to help your body function.

Down

1. The part of digestion which involves the grinding and moving along of food through the digestive canal.
2. A flap of cartilage in the back of your throat that drops down over the larynx and prevents food from going down the larynx.
3. The part of the digestive tract where feces (waste material) is formed. It is then evacuated from the body.
4. Another name for the gastrointestinal tract, where food passes through your body.
5. The hardest substance in your body, covering the outer layer of your teeth.
8. Chemicals inside your body, produced by your body, that help break food down into smaller components.

Copywork

Open wide your mouth and
I will fill it.

Psalm 81:10

Open wide your mouth and I will fill it.

Psalm 81:10

DIGESTION MINIBOOK
LESSON 4

Paste your Digestion
Pocket onto this page.

Antacid Experiment

Using hydrochloric acid, which is very similar to stomach acid, you can test which antacids work best to reduce acid indigestion. You will need to dissolve several different antacids (with the same milligram content) in warm water. Fill several beakers with the same amount of hydrochloric acid. Test each beaker with a different antacid, determining which one worked more quickly and effectively to neutralize the acid.

How do Enzymes Work?

A special enzyme called Papain is found in meat tenderizers. Let's do an experiment to see how this enzyme affects meat.

You will need:
1/4 cup of lunch meat
1 tsp of meat tenderizer
2 small jars with lids
Water

Put half of the meat in one jar. Add enough water to cover the meat. Put the lid on the jar and label it "water." Put the rest of the meat in the other jar. Cover it with the same amount of water. Add one teaspoon of meat tenderizer to the water. Put the lid on the jar and label it "Papain." Observe the jars for two days and record what you learn.

Digestion Differences

Do some research to learn about the different kinds of animal digestion. Be sure to study the digestion of ruminating animals, such as cows and deer, and also some unusual digestive habits of animals such as rabbits. Do a comparison and contrast between humans and these animals.

Book Suggestions

Disgusting Digestion by Nick Arnold. This book is written in a funny style, detailing lots of facts and information about digestion and the history of medicine as it relates to the topic.

What Happens to Your Food by Usborne Books. Watch how your food slips and slides through your body with this amazing book! Lift the flaps to find out what happens inside when you eat.

Why do People Eat? by Usborne Books. The simple text and detailed illustrations combine to answer questions related to why people eat. Answers are presented in clear, step-by-step stages and provide a wealth of information for the young reader.

My Digestion Projects
Lesson 4

What I did:

What I did:

What I learned:

What I learned:

If you follow my decrees and are careful to obey my commands, I will send you rain in its season, and the ground will yield its crops and the trees of the field their fruit.

Leviticus 26:3-4

I am the LORD your God, who brought you up out of Egypt. Open wide your mouth and I will fill it.

Psalm 81:10

NUTRITION
LESSON 5

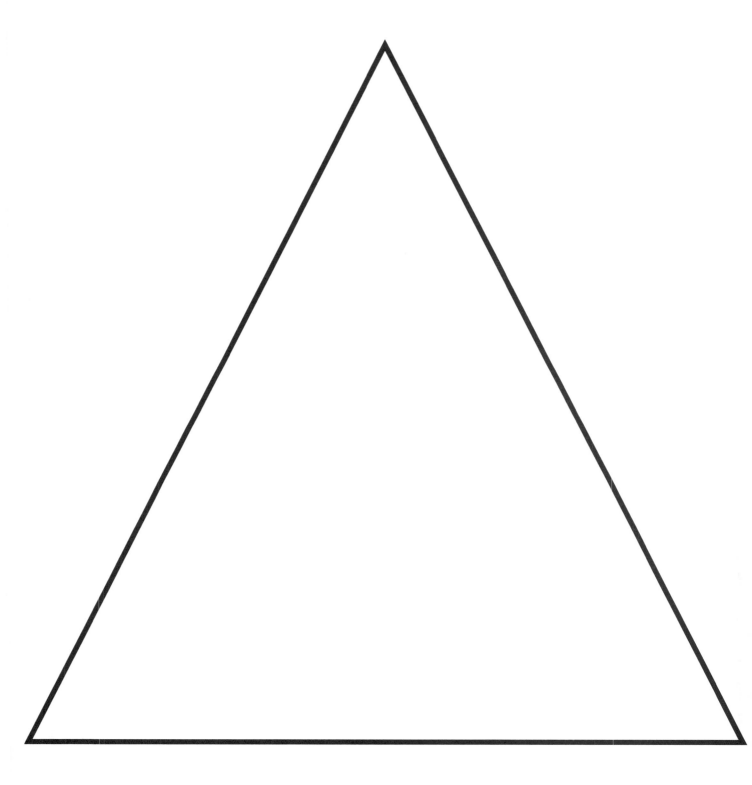

My Menus

Here you will make a pocket in which to keep all your menus. Cut a sheet of construction paper in half and glue it over this text along the bottom and side edges of the rectangle. Do not glue down the top edge! Make copies of the menu template on the previous page, or go to the book extras page I told you about at the beginning of this book to download a copy you can print from your printer. You can also create your own menu templates. Be sure to save all your menus in this pocket. You'll want to refer to them for future meals!

But solid food is for the mature,
who by constant use have trained
themselves to distinguish good
from evil.   Hebrews 5:14

But solid food is for the mature,
who by constant use have trained
themselves to distinguish good from evil.
Hebrews 5:14

VOCABULARY LIFT THE FLAP
LESSON 5

Tear out this page. Cut out each word and match it to the correct definition on the following page. Then, place glue along the top edge of the back of each word and glue above the line on each definition. Once the glue is dry, fold back the word to reveal the definition.

CALORIES

PROTEINS

NUTRIENTS

CARBOHYDRATES

ATOMS

MOLECULES

ESSENTIAL FATTY ACIDS

VITAMIN DEFICIENCY

NUTRITION VOCABULARY
LESSON 5

Glue correct word above this line, then fold back.

Carbon, hydrogen and oxygen atoms that are linked together and broken down to give your body the energy it needs.

Glue correct word above this line, then fold back.

A condition or disease that occurs when your body doesn't get the proper amount of a vitamin it needs.

Glue correct word above this line, then fold back.

Substances found in foods and drinks that your body needs to be healthy.

Glue correct word above this line, then fold back.

Fatty acids that you need that your body can't make.

Glue correct word above this line, then fold back.

The very smallest particles of an element. Everything you see is made from atoms.

Glue correct word above this line, then fold back.

Strands of amino acids that are found in every cell in your body that help to keep your body running smoothly.

Glue correct word above this line, then fold back.

Units we use to measure energy.

Glue correct word above this line, then fold back.

Two or more different kinds of atoms linked together.

NUTRITION MINIBOOK
LESSON 5

Paste your Nutrition
Matchbook onto this
page.

The Bible and Food

What does the Bible say about foods that are good for you? Read the story of Daniel and learn about the food he ate when he was taken into captivity. You can also study the different foods mentioned in the Bible. Which foods are considered healthy and which are considered unhealthy? Why did God deem some clean and some unclean? Organize your findings into a report and present it to your family.

People in the Bible grew their own food. Did it taste better than the store bought food we eat today? You can find out by growing some fruits and vegetables in your back yard. Do a taste test by comparing your home-grown food with the same food items from a grocery store. Which do your taste buds prefer: store bought or homegrown?

Vitamin C and Cold Prevention

Vitamin C is said to be effective against colds. Conduct an experiment to see whether taking vitamin C can prevent or lesson the symptoms associated with the common cold. Gather a large group of people. Instruct half of the group to take vitamin C every day for 30 days, and the other half not to take any vitamin C. Contact the people regularly during the 30 day period to see if they have experienced any cold symptoms. Note the severity of the symptoms. At the end of the 30 days, compare the two groups. Write a summary of your findings about the effectiveness of vitamin C for cold prevention. If done correctly, this could be a great science fair project.

Plants and Vitamins

The nutrients we feed plants are like vitamins for the plants. You can conduct an experiment to identify which brand of food is best for plants. You can also experiment to find out which types of nutrients are best for plants. You will need three identical plants in identical soil and containers, placed in the same spot and watered the exact same amount. You will also need two kinds of plant food. One of the three plants will be your control plant, receiving no food at all. The other two should be tested with one kind of plant food each. After a time, measure the plants' growth and color (inductive and deductive data) and record which plant fared best.

Cookbooks for Kids

The Gastrokid Cookbook by Hugh Garvey and Matthew Yeomans. This cookbook is for the kid who's willing to boldly explore new culinary tastes and experiences!

New Junior Cookbook: Better Homes and Gardens. The adult version of this "red and white checked" cookbook was the staple of my parents' kitchen and is a staple in mine as well.

Southern Living Kids Cookbook by Southern Living. This cookbook contains 124 recipes that kids will love to cook and eat!

"C" is for Cooking: Recipes from the Street by Susan McQuillan. Every recipe in this cookbook highlights at least one task that a young child can perform.

My Nutrition Projects
Lesson 5

What I did:

What I did:

What I learned:

What I learned:

SCIENTIFIC SPECULATION SHEET

Testing for Vitamin C

Lesson 5

Name_____   Date _____

Materials Used:

Procedure:

Hypothesis:

Results:

Conclusion:

The LORD God formed the man from the dust of the ground and breathed into his nostrils the breath of life, and the man became a living being.   Genesis 2:7

The Spirit of God has made me; the breath
of the Almighty gives me life.   Job 33:4

THE RESPIRATORY SYSTEM
LESSON 6

THE RESPIRATORY SYSTEM
LESSON 6

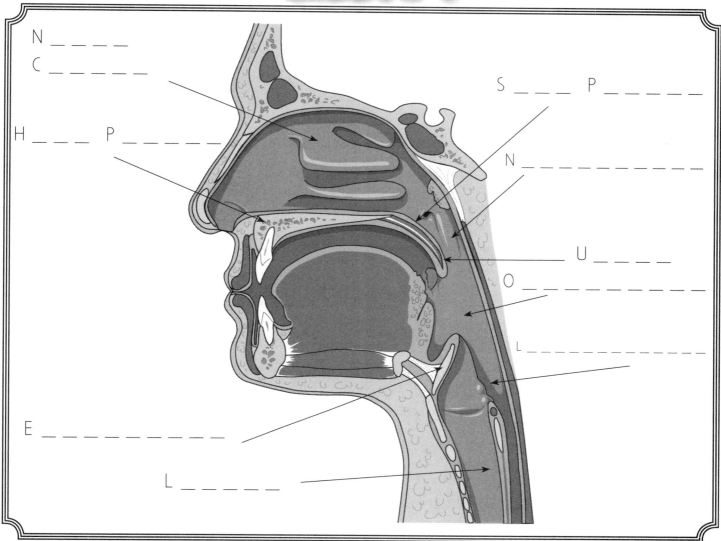

N _ _ _ _ _ _

C _ _ _ _ _ _

H _ _ _ _ _ _   P _ _ _ _ _ _ _ _ _

S _ _ _ _ _ P _ _ _ _ _ _

N _ _ _ _ _ _ _ _ _

U _ _ _ _ _

O _ _ _ _ _ _ _ _ _ _

L _ _ _ _ _ _ _ _ _ _ _ _

E _ _ _ _ _ _ _ _ _ _ _ _

L _ _ _ _ _ _ _

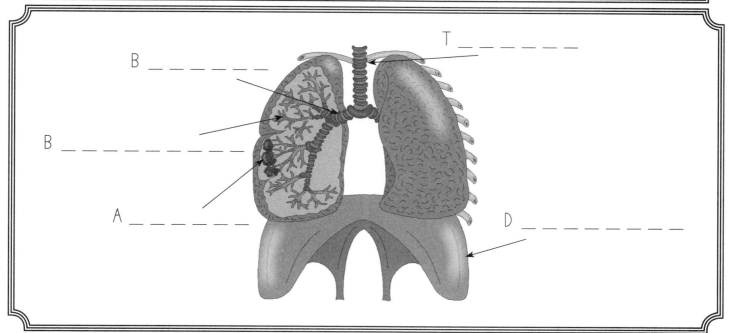

T _ _ _ _ _ _

B _ _ _ _ _ _ _ _ _

B _ _ _ _ _ _ _ _ _

A _ _ _ _ _ _ _ _

D _ _ _ _ _ _ _

SMOKING SPEECH
LESSON 6

_____

- -

_____

- -

_____

- -

_____

- -

_____

- -

_____

- -

_____

- -

_____

- -

_____

- -

_____

- -

_____

- -

_____

- -

_____

Anatomy Identification

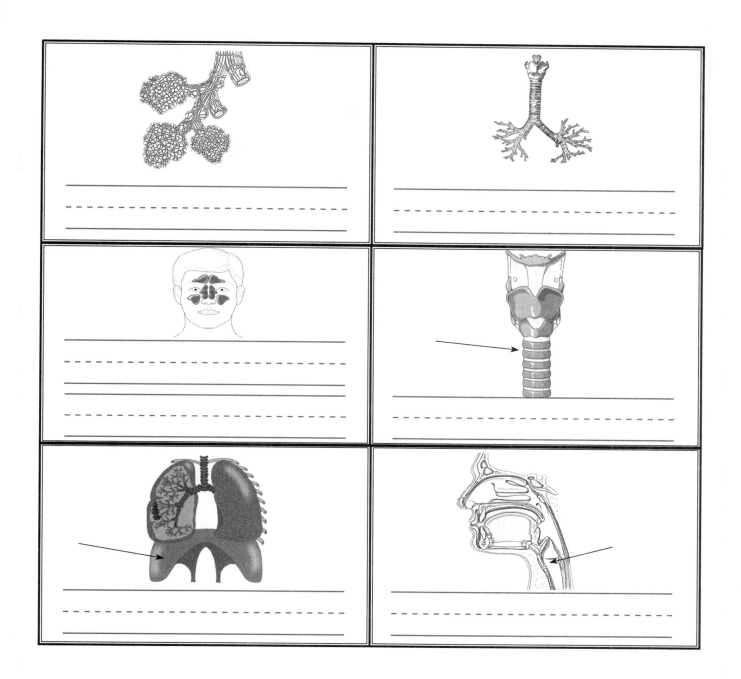

Write the correct names under the pictures.

Alveoli

Nasal Cavities

Diaphragm

Trachea

Larynx

Bronchi

91

Let everything that has
breath praise the LORD.
Psalm 150:6

Copywork

Let everything that has breath praise the LORD.

Psalm 150:6

Respiratory Minibooks
LESSON 6

Paste your Respiratory
Minibooks onto this
page.

What Does the Bible say About Breath?

Look up the word "breath" in your concordance and study the use of the word in the Bible. What does God's Word say about breath? When was the word first used? Write about your findings and share them with your family.

How Many Breaths?

Compare how many breaths you take when you're resting to how many breaths you take after exercising. Count the number of times you inhale in one minute. Then, do jumping jacks for one minute. Stop and count how many breaths you take in one minute after exercising. Is there a difference? Can you explain why?

Molecule Movement

Write a story about a molecule of oxygen that moves from the air, into your mouth, down your trachea and into your lungs. Where does it go? What does it think? How does it feel about how it is being used? You might even begin with where it was made (possibly by a plant). Have fun with your story!

Blue Breath

The air you breathe in is filled with oxygen, but do you have oxygen in the air you breathe out? If so, how much oxygen comes out of your breath along with the carbon dioxide? Let's find out! When you exhale carbon dioxide, if it mixes with water, it will form a weak acid called carbonic acid. This acid turns into a substance called bromothymol blue. Let's do an activity to find out if you breathe out more carbon dioxide after exercising.

You will need:
A glass
A straw
Bromothymol blue (can be purchased from pet stores)
A timer

Fill the glass with water. Add four drops of bromothymol blue to the water. (The water should be light blue.) Place the straw in the water. Now take a deep breath, then exhale into the straw. (DO NOT DRINK THIS WATER!) What happened to the water?

Now, run in place for five minutes and repeat the same activity. What happens when you blow in the water after exercising? Why do you think this happens?

My Respiratory Projects
Lesson 6

What I did:

What I did:

What I learned:

What I learned:

And they overcame him because of the
blood of the Lamb and because of the word
of their testimony, and they did not love
their life even when faced with death.

Revelation 12:11

And according to the Law, one may almost say, all things are cleansed with blood, and without shedding of blood there is no forgiveness. Hebrews 9:22

BLOOD
LESSON 7

BLOOD COMPONENTS

Red Blood Cells   **White Blood Cells**   **Platelets**   **Plasma**

APOLOGIA of FAITH
Lesson 7

Vocabulary Puzzle Game

Leukocytes

Circulatory System

The special oxygen carrying protein that red blood cells make and use. It also gives the red blood cells their red color.

Anemia

Another name for red blood cells.

Phagocytes

Cut out each puzzle piece on this page and the next. Match each vocabulary word puzzle piece to the correct definition puzzle piece. Cut out this rectangle and glue it to your Puzzle Page along the bottom and side edges to create a pocket. After you've played your Vocabulary Puzzle Game a few times, place all your puzzle pieces in the pocket for safe keeping.

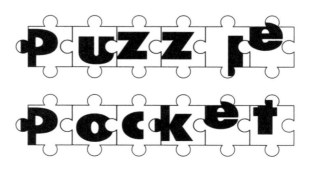

Hemoglobin

Erythrocytes

A condition that is commonly the result of not having enough iron in the body.

The system that carries your blood throughout your body.

Another name for white blood cells.

Special white blood cells that eat dangerous or worn-out cells.

Paste your puzzle pocket here.

But now in Christ Jesus you who
formerly were far off have been
brought near by the blood of Christ.
Ephesians 2:13

But now in Christ Jesus you who formerly were far off have been brought near by the blood of Christ.

Ephesians 2:13

Blood Minibooks

Lesson 7

Paste your Blood Shutter
Books onto this page.

Study the Eternal Significance of Blood

Find out what the Bible says about the blood of Jesus. Look up the word "blood" in a concordance. Read the verses that talk about Jesus' blood. What is its significance? What did the blood of Jesus accomplish? Write about your findings and share them with someone who has never considered the eternal significance of Jesus' shed blood.

Research Blood

Use the Internet or your library to research different aspects of blood. Some interesting topics to research include: different diseases that are spread through the blood, various blood disorders or diseases (such as hemophilia or leukemia), and different white blood cell counts and what they mean. Organize your research into a report and present it to your family or homeschool group.

DVD Suggestion

Red River of Life: Moody Science Classics Series. In this Christian DVD you'll learn about blood and how it carries oxygen to every part of your body. You'll also learn how the shed blood of Jesus Christ is the source of eternal life. (Elementary and up- 30 minutes)

My Blood Project
Lesson 7

What I did:

What I learned:

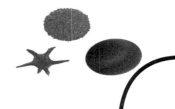

I will give you a new heart and put a new spirit in you;
I will remove from you your heart of stone and give
you a heart of flesh.   Ezekiel 36:26

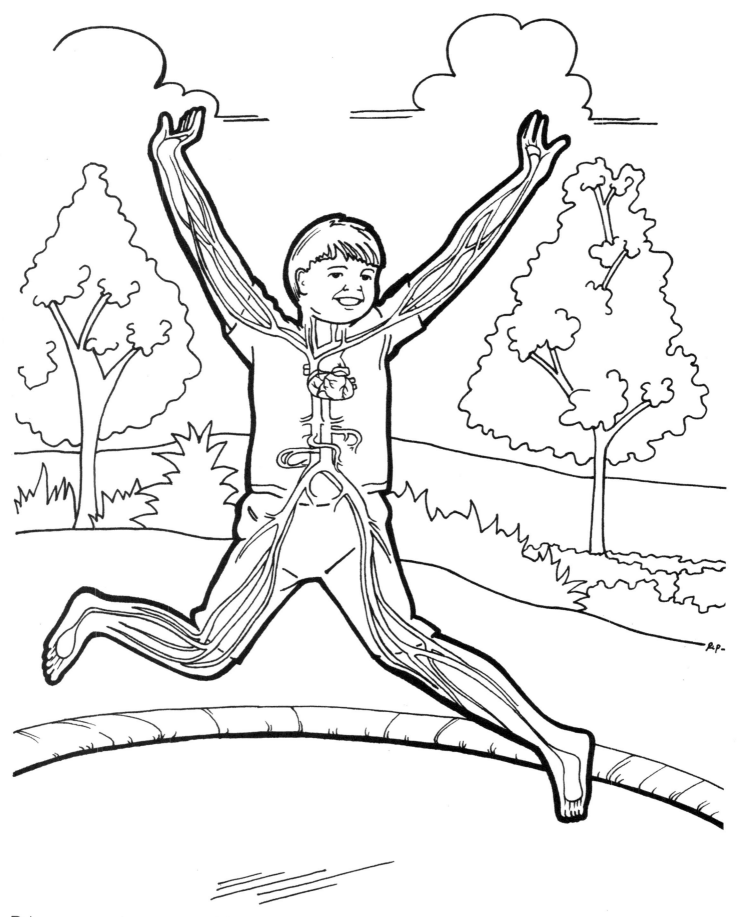

Blessed are the pure in heart, for they shall see God.
Matthew 5:8

The CARDIOVASCULAR SYSTEM

LESSON 8

_____

- - - - - - - - - - - - - - - - - - -

_____

_____

- - - - - - - - - - - - - - - - - - -

_____

Label the following parts of the heart:

Right Ventricle   Aorta
Right Atrium   Pulmonary Vein
Left Ventricle   Pulmonary Artery
Left Atrium   Superior Vena Cave
Inferior Vena Cava

Color the chambers and vessels that contain deoxygenated blood blue.
Color the chambers and vessels that contain oxygenated blood red.
Use arrows to indicate the path that blood takes as it travels
into the heart, out the pulmonary arteries, back into
the heart from the pulmonary veins, and out from the aorta.

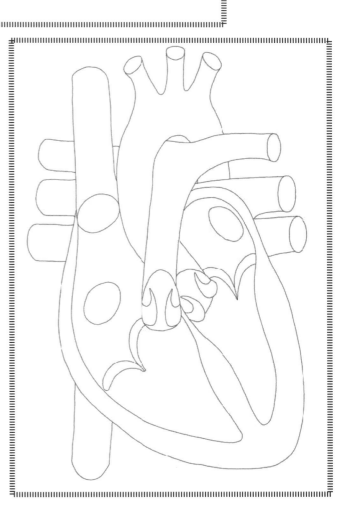

113

VOCABULARY LIFT THE FLAP
LESSON 8

Tear out this page. Cut out each word and match it to the correct definition on the following page. Then, place glue along the top edge of the back of each word and glue above the line on each definition. Once the glue is dry, fold back the word to reveal the definition.

ATRIUM	VENTRICLES
AORTA	INFERIOR VENA CAVA
SUPERIOR VENA CAVA	PULMONARY ARTERIES
PULMONARY VEINS	BLOOD PRESSURE

CARDIOVASCULAR VOCABULARY
LESSON 8

Glue correct word above this line, then fold back.

One of the top chambers of the heart.

Glue correct word above this line, then fold back.

The two lower chambers of the heart. These muscular chambers push the blood around your body.

Glue correct word above this line, then fold back.

Veins that carry oxygenated blood from the lungs to the heart.

Glue correct word above this line, then fold back.

A measurement of the force of the blood pushing against the walls of the arteries.

Glue correct word above this line, then fold back.

The largest artery in the body. It carries oxygenated blood away from the heart to arteries serving the body.

Glue correct word above this line, then fold back.

The large vein that collects blood from the lower parts of the body.

Glue correct word above this line, then fold back.

The large vein that collects blood from the upper parts of the body.

Glue correct word above this line, then fold back.

The only arteries that carry deoxygenated blood (blood that has a lower level of oxygen in it). They carry blood from the right ventricle to the lungs.

"Do not let your heart be troubled; believe in God, believe also in Me."

John 14:1

"Do not let your heart be troubled; believe in God, believe also in Me."

John 14:1

Cardiovascular Minibooks

LESSON 8

Paste your Cardio Tuck
In Envelopes onto this
page.

What Does the Bible say About the Heart?

God's word has a lot to say about the heart. Use a concordance to find all the references to the heart in the Bible. Read all the verses over the next week. Which verses speak to you most? Write about them in your journal or copy them onto index cards and memorize them. Be sure to share at least one of the verses with a friend or family member.

Find Your Resting Heart Rate

The resting heart rate of a healthy adult is between 60-100 beats per minute. Youths are known to have resting heart rates well over 100 beats per minute. People who exercise consistently have lower heart rates than those who don't exercise. Why do you think that is?

Make a Model of the Human Heart with Clay

Although this may be a bit difficult to get just right, use different colored clay to make an exterior model of the human heart. Be sure to include the veins and arteries leading in and out of the heart.

Heart Dissection

If you're really brave you can watch a heart being disassembled! Do an Internet search for: heart dissection. You will find links to videos of different types of heart dissections. How would you like to dissect a heart yourself! Check your homeschool group to see if they are offering a dissection lab for an animal's heart.

Write Your Own Zoe Story

You read the story of Zoe in this lesson. Now it's your turn to write your own story about a blood cell's journey through the body. Give your blood cell a name and a personality. Read back through the lesson to remember what you learned before you begin writing. Be creative and have fun describing the journey of a blood cell!

My Cardio Projects
Lesson 8

What I did:

What I did:

What I learned:

What I learned:

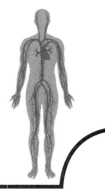

The mind of sinful man is death, but the mind controlled by the Spirit is life and peace.

Romans 8:b

For who has known the mind of the Lord that he may instruct him? But we have the mind of Christ.   1 Corinthians 2:16

NERVOUS AND ENDOCRINE SYSTEMS
LESSON 9

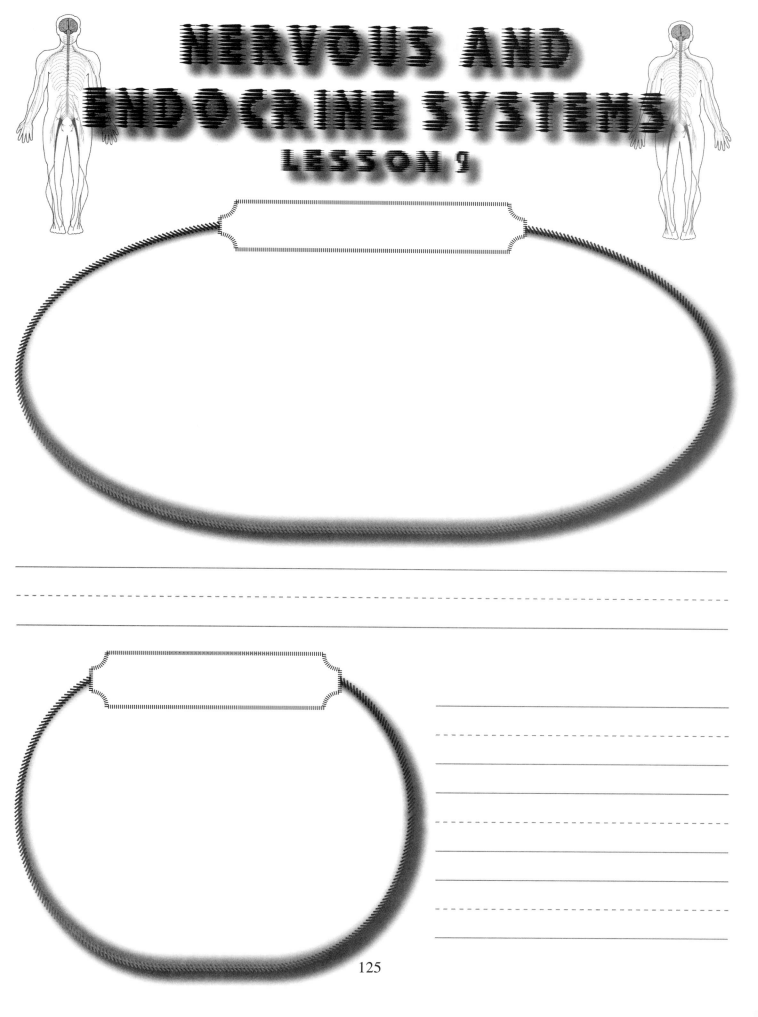

BRAIN

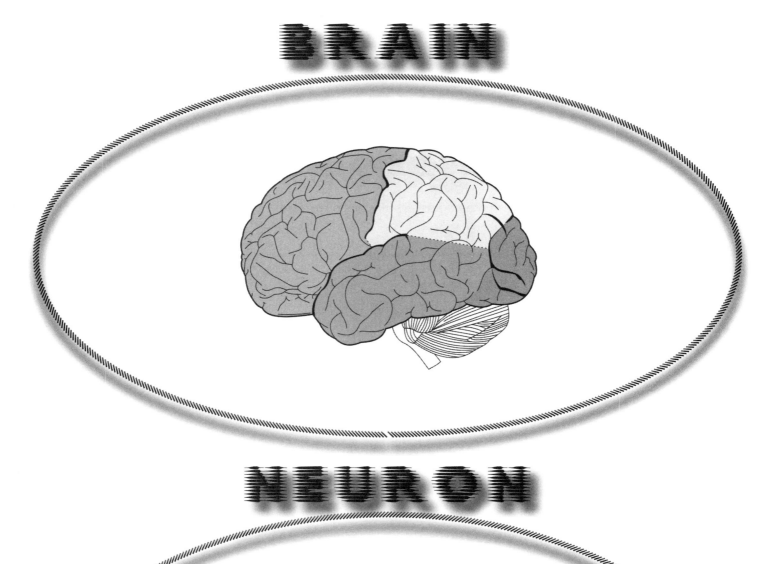

NEURON

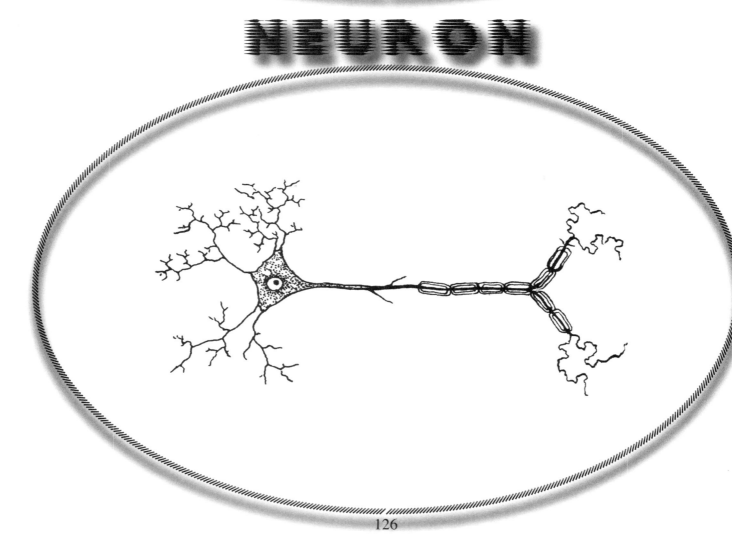

VENN DIAGRAM
LESSON 9

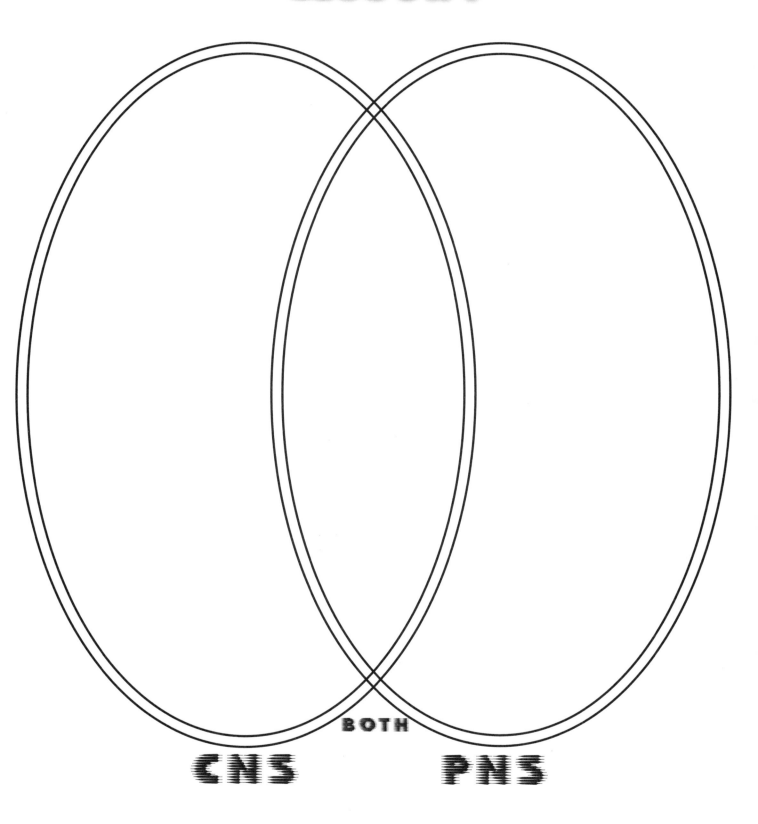

BOTH

CNS

PNS

Nervous System Hangers

You will need:
String (any kind will do)
Tape
Glue

Cut out the large title cards on this page and the small subtitle cards on the next. Color the images on the back of the small subtitle cards. You can also color the fronts of the cards if you'd like. Match the small cards to the correct large title cards by taping a 1-2 inch string to the back of the cards with tape. Place glue on the back of the large title cards and glue them to the correct "hanger" paste pages. Flip the subtitle cards to see the corresponding images on the back.

Central Nervous System

Brain

Neuron

Endocrine System

Brain	Spinal Cord
Cerebrum	Cerebellum
Brain Stem	Dendrite
Axon	Nucleus
Myelin Sheath	Thyroid Gland
Hormones	Pituitary Gland

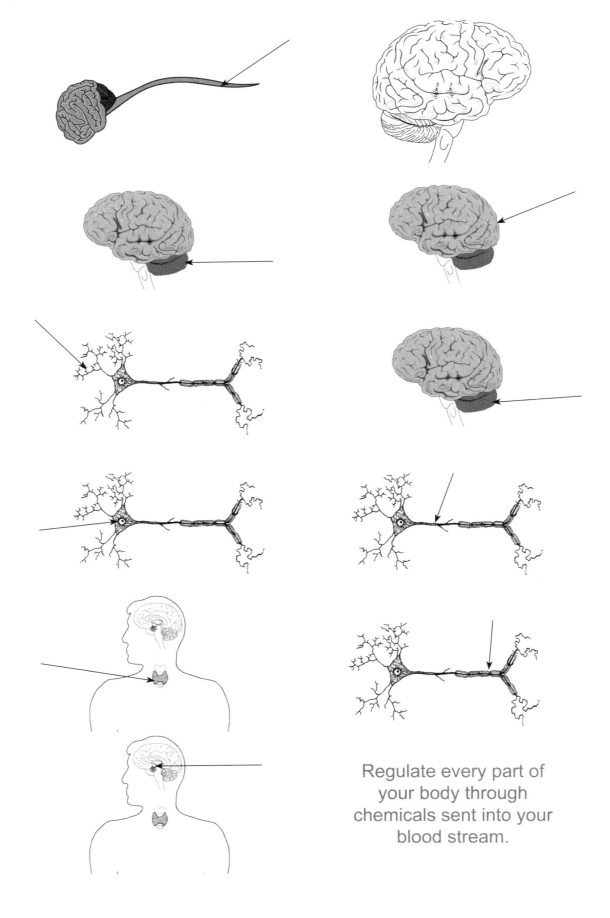

Regulate every part of
your body through
chemicals sent into your
blood stream.

132

Place Central Nervous System hanger here.

Place Brain hanger here.

Place Central Nervous System hanger here.

Place Neuron hanger here.

Place Endocrine System hanger here.

Copywork

You will keep in perfect peace
him whose mind is steadfast,
because he trusts in you.

Isaiah 26:3

You will keep in perfect peace him whose mind is steadfast, because he trusts in you.

Isaiah 26:3

NERVOUS SYSTEM MINIBOOK
LESSON 9

Paste your Nervous
System Layered Book
onto this page.

Test Your Auditory Memory

Here is an activity you can do with a friend to improve your brain function. Call out a series of six numbers. Can your friend recite the numbers exactly as you called them out? Now see if you can recite the six numbers your friend calls out. Most people can do six numbers. Not everyone can remember seven. Very, very few people can recite nine numbers that are called out. With practice, you might be able to build up to nine!

Test Your Visual Memory

Cut out 1 inch x 1 inch squares of different colored construction paper. You will need 15 squares of each color: red, blue, yellow, white and black.

Sit across from your friend and put a folder on the table between you. Place the folder in an open upright position (like a tent) so that your friend cannot see you place the colored squares. Put six colored squares in any order. Then, carefully remove the folder. Give your friend three seconds to look at the squares. Now cover them up with a black piece of construction paper. Next, have your friend rebuild the squares in the order in which you put them. Of course, your friend's squares will be opposite your order because your friend was seeing them backwards. Once your friend is done, lift up the black piece of paper and compare. If your friend was successful, let her give you a chance to do it. This time try with seven squares. Then try with eight. To make things even more challenging, place the squares in a unique pattern or shape. Also, you can reduce the time allowed for looking at the pattern. Or, if a three second look is too challenging, you can increase the amount of time for looking and slowly decrease it as you build your skills.

Build Your Brain

Research has shown that challenging the mind with games and activities that require a great deal of mental processing can actually keep people from aging mentally. It can also improve a person's overall cognitive or thinking ability. It's just like physical exercise. If you exercise your brain, it will grow stronger. Additionally, studies suggest that if you do not exercise your brain, you will lose valuable brain functioning, perhaps permanently. Yet, we can actually grow neural pathways at any age. So, although you need to use it or lose it, if you work hard, you can grow your brain! That's another reason to learn as much as you can and try to remember what you learned. Why not begin learning some of the games and participating in some of the activities that have shown to develop neural pathways? Here are some suggestions:

Learn to play Chess

Learn to play Bridge

Learn to play Sudoku

Listen to Classical Music

Learn to play an instrument

Learn a foreign language

Learn a new sport

My Nervous System Projects
Lesson 9

What I did:

What I did:

What I learned:

What I learned:

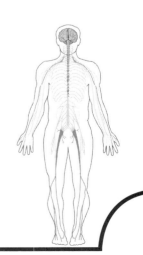

Thou wilt keep him in perfect peace, whose mind is stayed on thee: because he trusteth in thee.

Isaiah 26: 3

Do not conform any longer to the pattern of this world,
but be transformed by the renewing of your mind. Then you
will be able to test and approve what God's will is his good,
pleasing and perfect will.   Romans 12:2

NERVOUS SYSTEM EXTENDED

LESSON 10

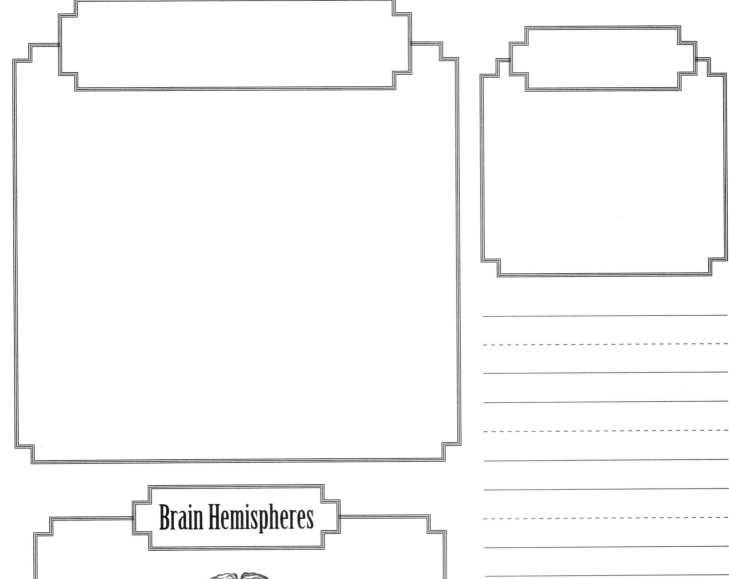

Brain Hemispheres

CEREBRAL LOBES

LESSON 10

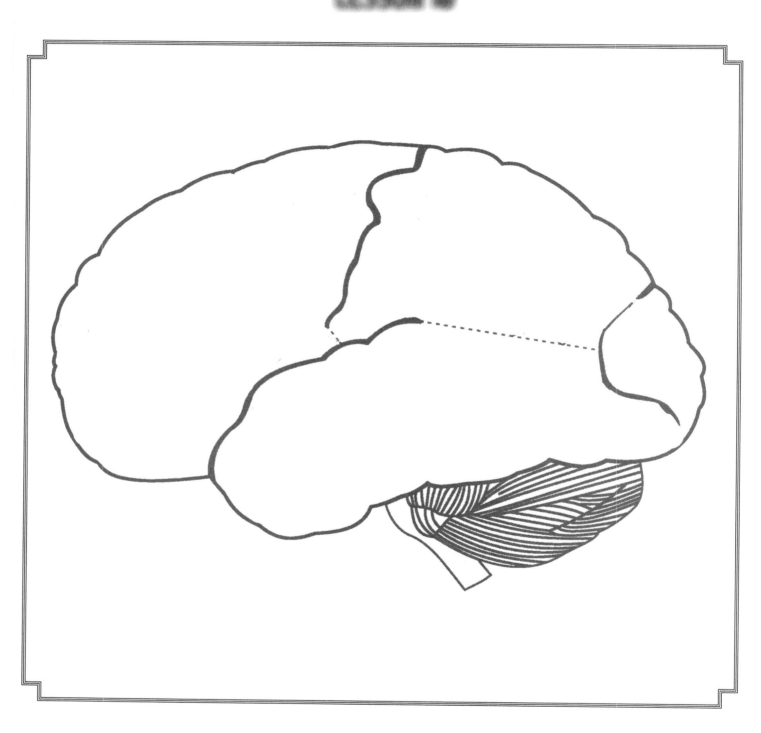

Frontal Lobe   **Temporal Lobe**   **Occipital Lobe**   **Parietal Lobe**

Anatomy Identification

Write the correct names under the pictures.

Parietal Lobe	Frontal Lobe	Occipital Lobe
Spinal Cord	Temporal Lobe	Nerves

For to be carnally
minded is death; but to
be spiritually minded is
life and peace.

Romans 8:6

For to be carnally minded is
death; but to be spiritually
minded is life and peace.

Romans 8:6

BRAIN MINIBOOK
LESSON 10

Paste your Brain Book
onto this page.

Creative Writing Assignment

Write a newspaper article describing what your brain did today. You can read the sports page for ideas on how to describe the play by play actions. Tell your readers which players (parts of the brain) did what during the day.

Foot Dominance

You probably know whether you are right- or left-handed, but are you right- or left-footed? Are you right- or left-eyed? Are you right- or left-eared? All these things are dominated by a particular side of your brain. Let's find out which you are.

To find out if you are right- or left-footed, find an open space and try to do a cartwheel. With which foot did you begin? If it's the opposite of your handedness, then see which foot you prefer when kicking a ball. You can be ambidextrous, or have both feet dominant at different times.

Eye Dominance

Do you know which eye takes command when you are seeing? Look at something far away. Then, line up one of your fingers with that object to block it out. Now, keeping your finger there, close one eye, then the other. When you close your weaker eye, the object will remain blocked. However, when you open and close your "seeing" or dominant eye, your finger will jump back and forth.

Here's another way to find out. Cut a 1 inch circle out of the middle of a piece of notebook paper. Now, using both eyes, look through the hole in the paper at a distant object. Now, bring the paper closer and closer to your face while you are still keeping the distant object in focus. To which eye did you bring the paper? That's your dominant eye!

Ear Dominance

You also have a dominant ear. Let's see which one hears the best. If your friend says she needs to tell you a secret as she comes toward you, which ear do you give her?

Now, imagine you want to listen to a conversation in another room through the wall. Which ear do you put up to the wall? That's your dominant ear!

My Nervous System Projects
Lesson 10

What I did:

What I did:

What I learned:

What I learned:

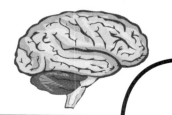

Since ancient times no one has heard, no ear has perceived, no eye has seen any God besides you, who acts on behalf of those who wait for him.

Isaiah 64:4

If the whole body were an eye, where would the sense of hearing be? If the whole body were an ear, where would the sense of smell be?   1 Corinthians 12:17

SENSES
LESSON 11

O _ _ _ _ _ _ _ _ _   B _ _ _ _

O _ _ _ _ _ _ _ _ _
E _ _ _ _ _ _ _ _ _

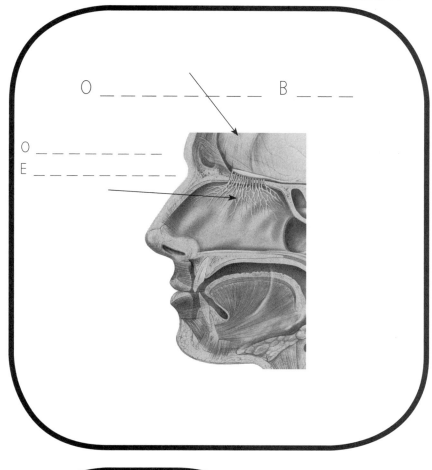

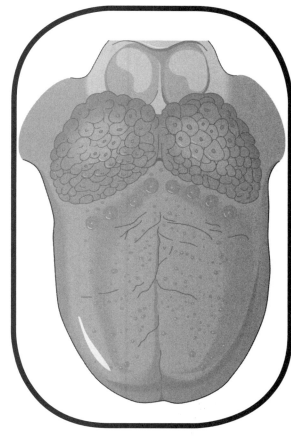

SENSES
LESSON 11

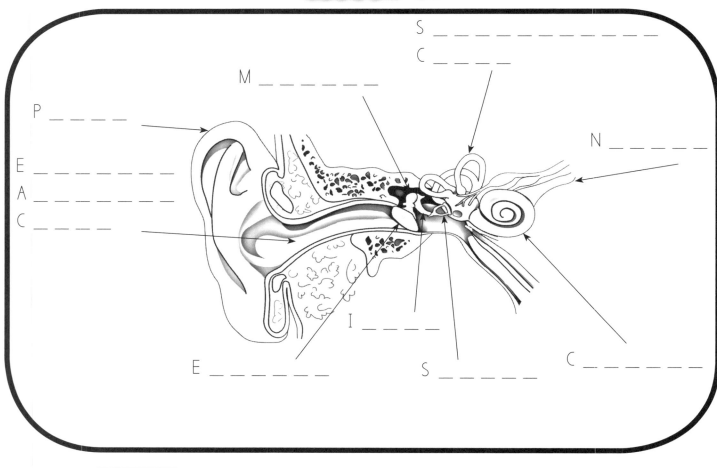

S _ _ _ _ _ _ _ _ _ _ _ _ _

C _ _ _ _ _ _

M _ _ _ _ _ _ _

P _ _ _ _ _

E _ _ _ _ _ _ _ _

A _ _ _ _ _ _ _

C _ _ _ _

N _ _ _ _ _ _

E _ _ _ _ _ _ _

I _ _ _ _ _ _

S _ _ _ _ _ _

C _ _ _ _ _ _ _

DIAGRAM OF EYE
LESSON 11

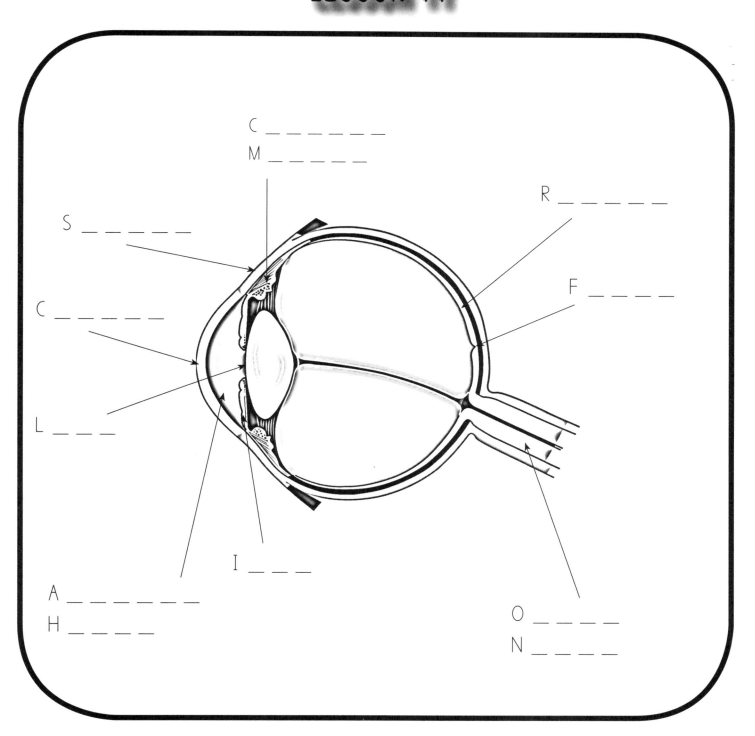

C _ _ _ _ _ _ _
M _ _ _ _ _ _
R _ _ _ _ _ _
S _ _ _ _ _ _
C _ _ _ _ _
F _ _ _ _ _
L _ _ _ _
I _ _ _ _
A _ _ _ _ _ _ _ _
H _ _ _ _ _
O _ _ _ _ _
N _ _ _ _ _

Retina   **Fovea**   **Cornea**

Ciliary Muscle **Optic Nerve**   **Sclera**

Aqueous Humor   **Iris**   **Lens**

I will counsel you with My
eye upon you.

Psalm 32:8

I will counsel you with My eye upon you.

Psalm 32:8

ANATOMY MATCH UP
LESSON 11

Cut out the vocabulary terms below and glue them inside the correct boxes on the following pages.

ODOR	EARDRUM	MACULA	NOSTRIL
SALTY	OLFACTORY EPITHELIUM	RODS	RETINA
SEMICIRCULAR CANALS	CORNEA	PUPIL	SWEET
IRIS	PAPILLAE	SNIFF	OTOLITHS
CILIA	PINNA	LENS	SALIVA
VESTIBULE	SOUR	TASTE BUDS	OLFACTORY SYSTEM

ANATOMY MATCH UP
LESSON 11

Smelling	Tasting
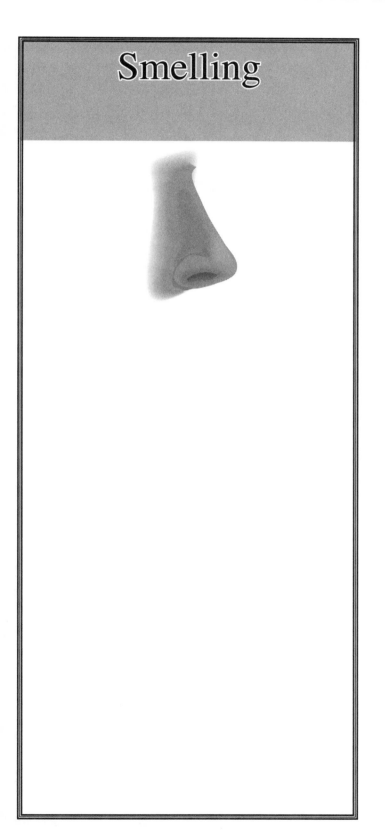	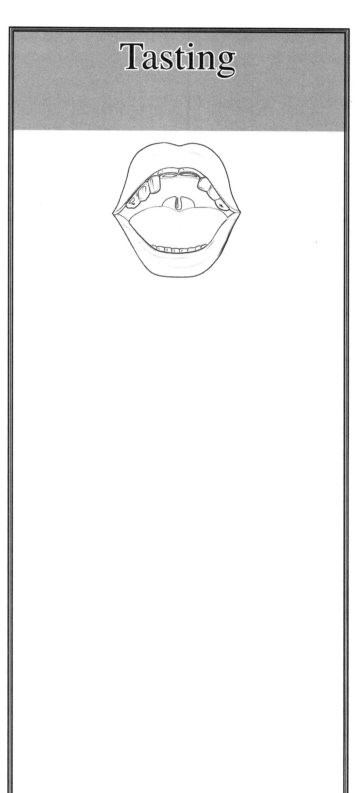

Hearing
Balancing

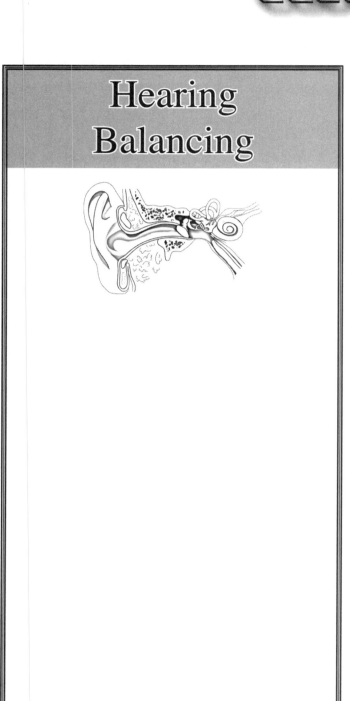

Seeing

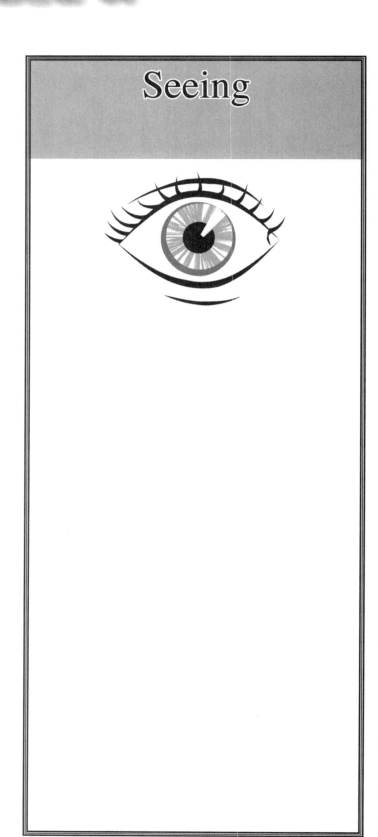

SENSES MINIBOOK
LESSON 11

Paste your Five Senses
Tab Book onto this page.

What Does the Bible say About the Eyes?

The Bible talks about the eyes quite a bit. Use a concordance to find and read all the verses that talk about the eyes. Write down what you learn about eyes as you read. How can your eyes aid in or hinder your spiritual life?

Make an Ear Drum Model

Make a model of your ear drum with an empty bathroom tissue tube, a balloon big enough to fit over it and a rubber band. Cut the thin portion off the balloon and stretch it over one end of the tube. Secure it with a rubber band. Now, put your finger on the balloon and speak through the other end of the tube. Can you feel the balloon vibrate? This is how your eardrum works.

You can extend this activity by making an entire model of the ear. You might use clay to form the inner ear organs, and craft supplies to make the bones.

Follow Your Nose

With another partner, see if you can locate where a smell comes from without the use of your eyes. Place strong aromas, such as perfume and vanilla, on cotton balls. Have your friend hide the cotton around a large room. With a blindfold on, see how long it takes you to locate the cotton balls. Have your friend give it a try as well. Who has a better sense of smell?

Turn Off That Sound

You may not realize it, but your house is full of sounds that you have become accustomed to. Try turning off and unplugging every single electric item for one whole day. Be sure to get your parents' permission to do this. You will want to plug your refrigerator back in right away so that your food does not spoil. However, I believe you'll be amazed at how really quiet it is.

Field Trip to an Optometrist

Schedule a field trip to visit an optometrist in order to learn about what they do to evaluate people's vision and how they find the right glasses for people. You might even have your eyes checked while you are there!

Balance Activity

How good is your balance? How long can you stand on one leg? How long can you stand on one leg with your eyes closed? Do you see how your eyes work with your ears to keep you balanced?

Here's another activity to test your balance. Find a thin board that is about two feet long and a foot wide. Now get a full can of food from the kitchen cabinet. Place the board on top of the can and carefully, with the help of an adult, step on either side of the board trying to balance it on the can.

My Senses Projects
Lesson 11

What I did:

What I did:

What I learned:

What I learned:

Are not five sparrows sold for two pennies? Yet not one of them is forgotten by God. Indeed, the very hairs of your head are all numbered. Don't be afraid; you are worth more than many sparrows.   Luke 12:6-7

You, however, are not in the flesh but in the Spirit, if in fact the Spirit of God dwells in you.   Romans 8:9

THE INTEGUMENTARY SYSTEM
LESSON 12

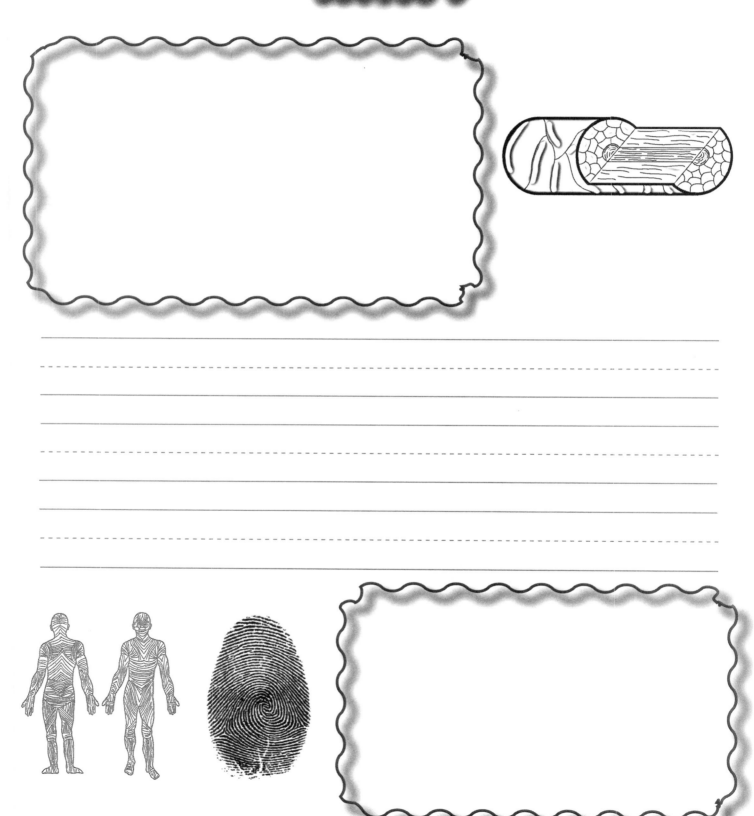

Diagram of Skin

Lesson 12

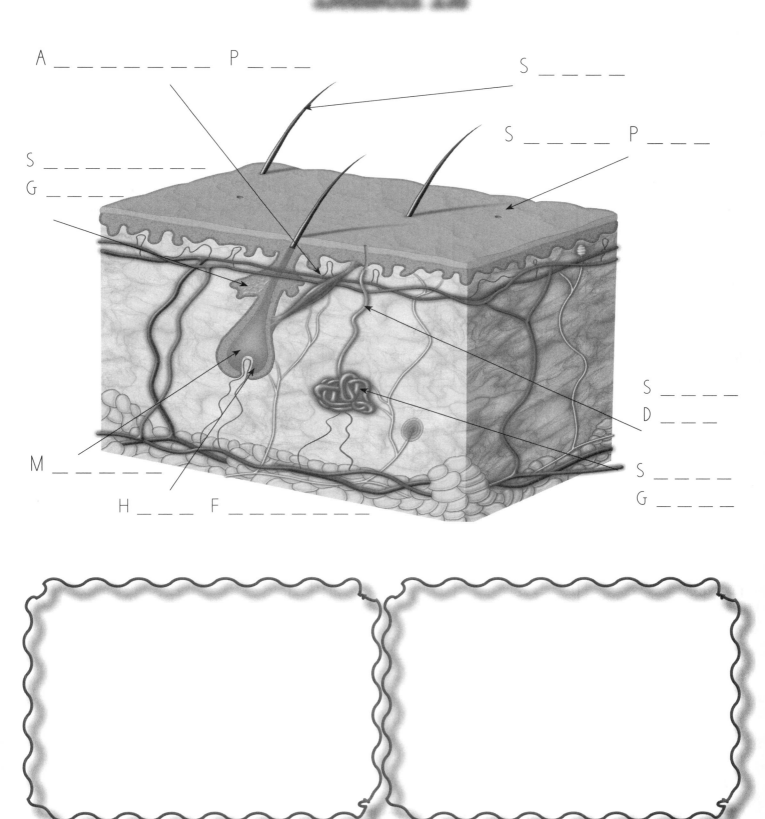

A _ _ _ _ _ _ _ _ _ P _ _ _ _   S _ _ _ _ _

S _ _ _ _ _   P _ _ _ _

S _ _ _ _ _ _ _ _
G _ _ _ _ _

S _ _ _ _ _
D _ _ _ _

M _ _ _ _ _ _   S _ _ _ _ _
G _ _ _ _

H _ _ _ _   F _ _ _ _ _ _ _ _

FINGERPRINTS
LESSON 12

LEFT PINKY	LEFT RING	LEFT MIDDLE	LEFT INDEX	LEFT THUMB

RIGHT THUMB	RIGHT INDEX	RIGHT MIDDLE	RIGHT RING	RIGHT PINKY

Braille Alphabet

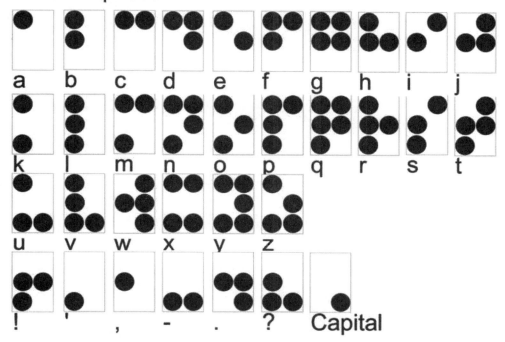

a	b	c	d	e	f	g	h	i	j
k	l	m	n	o	p	q	r	s	t
u	v	w	x	y	z				

!	'	,	-	.	?	Capital

Numbers

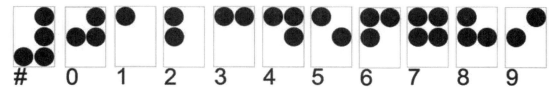

#	0	1	2	3	4	5	6	7	8	9

171

VOCABULARY LIFT THE FLAP
LESSON 12

Tear out this page. Cut out each word and match it to the correct definition on the following page. Then, place glue along the top edge of the back of each word and glue above the line on each definition. Once the glue is dry, fold back the word to reveal the definition.

INTEGUMENTARY SYSTEM	MELANIN
EPIDERMIS	DERMIS
SEBACEOUS GLANDS	CLEAVAGE LINES
HAIR FOLLICLE	LUNULA

SKIN VOCABULARY
LESSON 12

Glue correct word above this line, then fold back.

The half-moon shaped area of paleness beyond the cuticle of your nail. It is part of the nail matrix.

Glue correct word above this line, then fold back.

Patterns of indentions in your skin.

Glue correct word above this line, then fold back.

The outer layer of your skin.

Glue correct word above this line, then fold back.

Lots of this pigment will make skin brown, olive or black.

Glue correct word above this line, then fold back.

Oil glands that are like built-in skin lotion dispensers.

Glue correct word above this line, then fold back.

A little "pocket" from which hair grows.

Glue correct word above this line, then fold back.

The inner layer of your skin.

Glue correct word above this line, then fold back.

Your skin (along with your nails, hair, sweat glands, and oil glands) makes up this complex group of tissues.

Flesh gives birth to flesh,
but the Spirit gives birth
to spirit.

John 3:6

Flesh gives birth to flesh, but the Spirit gives birth to spirit.

John 3:6

INTEGUMENTARY MINIBOOK
LESSON 12

Paste your Skin Shield
Book onto this page.

How's Your Sense of Touch?

See how well your sense of touch works. Have a partner place objects in a paper bag. Close your eyes and reach in the bag. Can you identify what the objects are just by touching them? You can also play the game "What's in Ned's Head?" It's based on the same concept of using your sense of touch. Players race against one another to quickly and accurately find the different items placed inside Ned's Head. This fun family game can be purchased at your local toy store.

Examine Your Skin

Use a magnifying glass to study your skin up close. Do you see all the little holes in your skin? Do you see the tiny hairs?

Examine People's Hair

With their permission, take a strand of hair from each of your friends and family members. Try not to hurt them! Now, tape the strands to a sheet of paper and label to whom each strand belongs. Study the hairs under a magnifying glass or with a microscope. How do the strands differ? How are they the same?

Test Substances on Your Skin

Some substances stay on your skin's surface, while other substances are absorbed by your skin. Let's see what happens when you place four different substances on your skin.

You will need:
Lotion
Water
Alcohol
Oil

Make a hypothesis about what will happen to each substance when it is placed on your skin. Turn your arm upward so the inside of your arm is facing up. Now place your arm on a table in the upward position. Next, put one drop of each substance on your arm, keeping your arm very still. Watch what happens.

Crime Scene Investigation

You can purchase kits that allow you to lift fingerprints off of items (such as desks, cups, glasses, cans and such). This is a fun activity that will teach you a lot about Crime Scene Investigators. Check the Internet to find where to purchase the kits.

My Skin Projects
Lesson 12

What I did:

What I did:

What I learned:

What I learned:

SCIENTIFIC SPECULATION SHEET

Sensing Sensitivity

Lesson 12

Name_____   Date _____

Materials Used:

Procedure:

Hypothesis:

Results:

Conclusion:

Praise the LORD, O my soul, and forget not all his benefits;
who forgives all your sins and heals all your diseases; who
redeems your life from the pit and crowns you with love and
compassion.
                                                        Psalm 103:2-4

He personally carried our sins in his body on the cross so that we can be dead to sin and live for what is right. By his wounds you are healed.   I Peter 2:24

The Lymphatic and Immune Systems
Lesson 13

Pathogens

Immune System

The Lymphatic and Immune Systems
Lesson 13

Lymphatic System

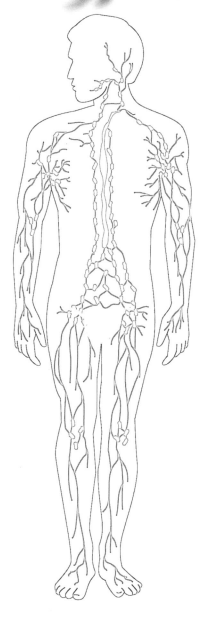

_____
- - - - - - - - - - - - - - - - - -
_____
_____
_____
- - - - - - - - - - - - - - - - - -
_____
_____
_____
- - - - - - - - - - - - - - - - - -
_____
_____
_____
- - - - - - - - - - - - - - - - - -
_____
_____
_____
- - - - - - - - - - - - - - - - - -
_____
_____
_____
- - - - - - - - - - - - - - - - - -
_____
_____

All the days ordained for me
were written in your book
before one of them came to be.
Psalm 139:16

All the days ordained for me were
written in your book before one of them
came to be.

Psalm 139:16

Vocabulary Puzzle Game

Immunity

Lymphatic System

A disease that is life threatening.

Pathogens

Immunity that we get from vaccinations.

Spleen

Cut out each puzzle piece on this page and the next. Match each vocabulary word puzzle piece to the correct definition puzzle piece. Cut out this rectangle and glue it to your Puzzle Page along the bottom and side edges to create a pocket. After you've played your Vocabulary Puzzle game a few times, place all your puzzle pieces in the pocket for safe keeping.

Glue along this edge

Glue along this edge

Glue along this edge

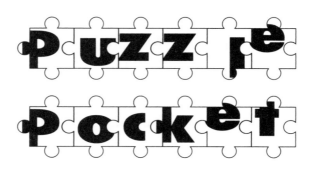

Malignant

Artificial Immunity

Microscopic germs that get inside your body and can potentially cause an infection.

The body's defense system that includes 500 small, bean-shaped filters located throughout the body. They produce white blood cells called lymphocytes that destroy invaders.

A system of defense against pathogens and cancers.

The largest of the lymph organs. Its main job is to filter blood.

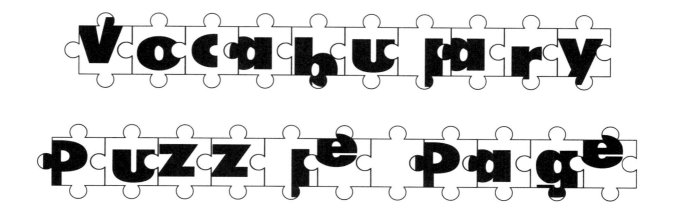

Vocabulary Puzzle Page

Paste your puzzle pocket here.

Defense Minibook
Lesson 13

Paste your Defense
Accordion Book onto
this page.

Participate in a Science Fair

Consider participating in a science fair with bacteria as your topic. Some possible things to study and explore are:

1. What methods are most effective in keeping a toothbrush free from bacteria?
2. Which mouthwash best fights bacteria?
3. Which cleaner is the most effective at eliminating bacteria?
4. Do any herbs inhibit bacteria growth? Which ones might?
5. Are tables at the local restaurant bacteria free?
6. How long does bacteria stay on toys?

Write a Book Report

There are many children's books on plagues, diseases, bacteria, animal bites and medicinal discoveries. Choose a topic and write a report that can be presented to your homeschool group.

Book Suggestions

Louis Pasteur: Founder of Modern Medicine by John Hudson Tiner. Focusing on the Christian character of Pasteur, this book supports the Biblical view of Creation.

Pasteur's Fight Against Microbes by Beverly Birch. This book has an abundance of beautiful illustrations and is comprehensive for elementary aged children.

An American Plague: The True and Terrifying Story of the Yellow Fever Epidemic of 1793 (Newberry Honor Book) by Jim Murphy. This powerful, dramatic account traces the devastating course of the epidemic.

Bubonic Plague by Jim Whiting. A historical account of the plague written for young elementary students.

Fever 1793 by Laurie Halse Anderson. This is a gripping story about a 14 yr. old girl who seeks to live morally amidst rampant death. The book has won many awards and is classified as Teen Middle.

What Makes You Ill? by Usborne Books. The simple text and detailed illustrations combine to answer questions related to what makes you ill. The answers are given in clear, step-by-step stages. Young readers will enjoy learning about germs and how to stay healthy.

My Lymphatic Project
Lesson 13

What I did:

What I learned:

SCIENTIFIC SPECULATION SHEET

Testing for Bacteria and Fungi

Lesson 13

Name_____   Date _____

Materials Used:

Procedure:

Hypothesis:

Results:

Conclusion:

And Jesus grew in wisdom and stature, and in favor with God and men. Luke 2:52

Therefore, I urge you, brothers, in view of God's mercy, to offer your bodies as living sacrifices, holy and pleasing to God--this is your spiritual act of worship.

Romans 12:1

GROWTH AND DEVELOPMENT

LESSON 14

GOD CREATED ME
LESSON 14

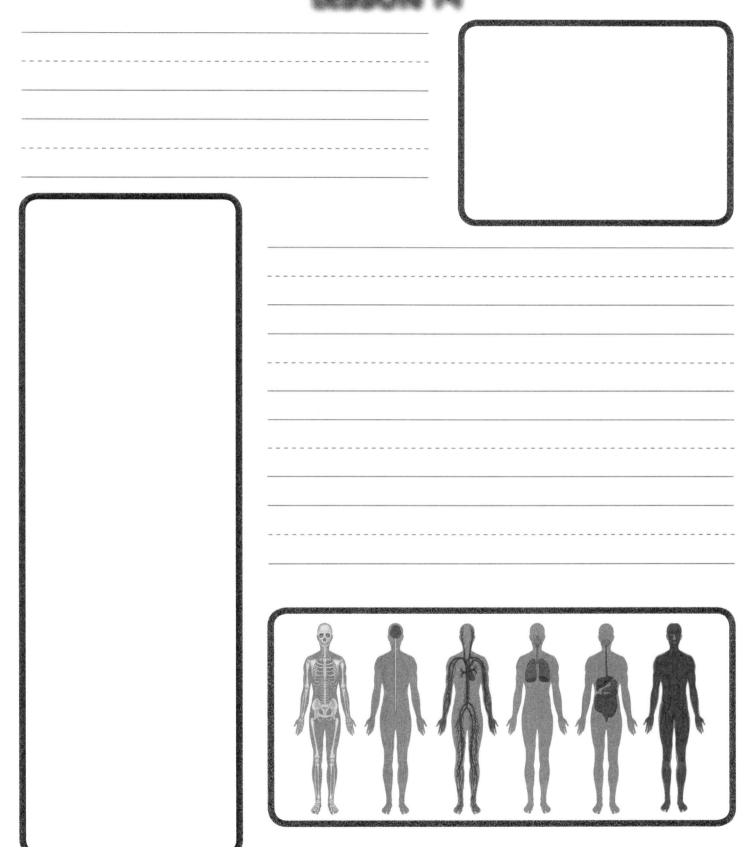

STAGES OF DEVELOPMENT
LESSON 14

Possible Purpose Page
Ephesians 2:10

My Strengths, Gifts and Talents

My Interests

How I can Glorify God with my Life

I will give thanks to You,

for I am fearfully and

wonderfully made;

Psalm 139:14

I will give thanks to You, for I
am fearfully and wonderfully made;

Psalm 139: 14

GROWTH AND DEVELOPMENT CROSSWORD

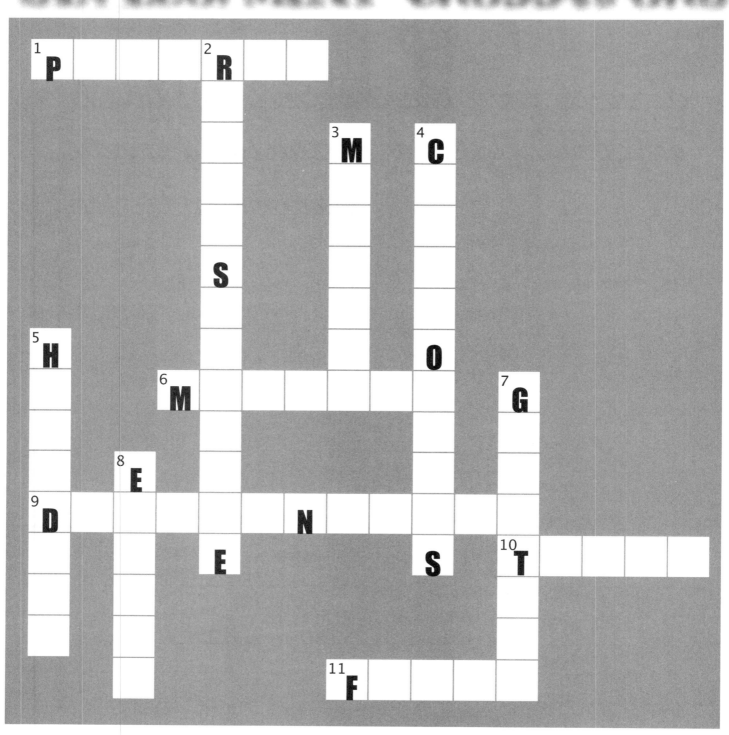

EMBRYO
PUBERTY
CHROMOSOMES
DOMINANT GENE
HEREDITY
FETUS

GENETICS
TRAIT
MITOSIS
RECESSIVE GENE
MEIOSIS

GROWTH AND DEVELOPMENT CROSSWORD

Across

1. The period between the ages of 9 and 14 when the body begins taking on a more adult form, and the differences between males and females become more obvious.
6. A special cell division process that results in unique cells called gametes (they have half the regular number of chromosomes).
9. A gene that will determine a trait that one has.
10. A recognizable physical characteristic, like eye color, skin color, or hair texture.
11. What you were called when you were developing in your mother's womb *after* your first two months of life.

Down

2. A gene that is "sleeping." The trait will be masked by the dominant gene. The trait is still present in the DNA, but won't be part of the person's physical characteristics.
3. The process whereby a cell divides to make two new cells with exactly the same DNA as the original cell.
4. Your DNA splits into these 46 smaller units.
5. The passing on of traits from parents to their children.
7. The study of genes and heredity.
8. What you were called when you were developing in your mother's womb *during* your first two months of life.

GROWTH AND DEVELOPMENT MINIBOOK
LESSON 14

Paste your Growth and
Development Fan onto
this page.

Time Lines

If you have visited the same pediatrician for many years, he or she will have a record of your growth. You can ask the receptionist at your pediatrician's office for a copy of your growth charts (some will charge a small fee), and you can create a time line of your growth over the years.

You can also create a time line of your development by charting the ages at which you developed certain skills, such as: walking, talking, learning to read, riding a bike and such.

Another idea is to make a time line of your family. Search the Internet to find examples of time lines.

Make a Genetic Family Tree

Most family trees simply list names of family members. You can create your own family tree and make it really special by listing a unique trait for each family member. You can choose physical traits or character traits, or both! Do you see any similarities between family members? Which family member are you most like?

Study Genetics:
Wisconsin Fast Plants Study on Genetics: Hairy's Inheritance: Competing to Make the Hairiest Plant Kit

Here's a fun, competitive activity that will help you learn about genetics. During this study, you'll be competing to make the hairiest plant, so find a friend and let the competition begin! Each week you'll do an activity that focuses on raising and crossbreeding fast plants, with the goal of breeding an unusually hairy plant. Through this study, you'll learn a great deal about botany and caring for plants. You'll also explore pollination and will come to understand hybrid plants and many other scientific concepts related to genetics.

Book and DVD Suggestions

Gene Machines by Frances R. Balkwill and Mic Rolph. This book has one major flaw: the authors are seeking to indoctrinate students in evolutionary thought. They make a big deal over the number of genes humans have compared to other animals, and also how similar human organ systems are to those of mice. But you can avoid those discussions by skipping pages 20-23, unless you are prepared to discuss how similar design does not indicate a common ancestor, but a common Designer!

Gregor Mendel: The Friar Who Grew Peas by Cheryl Bardoe. A wonderful gem, with beautiful illustrations and a great story line unraveling DNA and genetics.

The Bible (Genesis chapter 30). Read the story of how Jacob tricked Laban by crossbreeding goats.

The Wonders of God's Creation: Human Life (Moody). In this DVD you'll learn about the Master Creator as you take a journey deep into the human body.

My Growth and Developmenopment Project
Lesson 14

What I did:

What I learned:

MY ANATOMY FIELD TRIP

Place: Date:

The purpose of this field trip:

What I saw/did on this trip:

What I learned:

My favorite part:

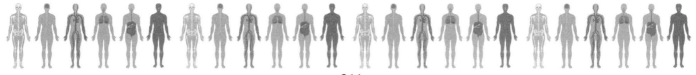

MY ANATOMY FIELD TRIP

Place: Date:

The purpose of this field trip:

What I saw/did on this trip:

What I learned:

My favorite part:

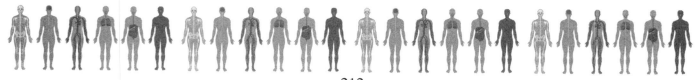

MY ANATOMY FIELD TRIP

Place: Date:

The purpose of this field trip:

What I saw/did on this trip:

What I learned:

My favorite part:

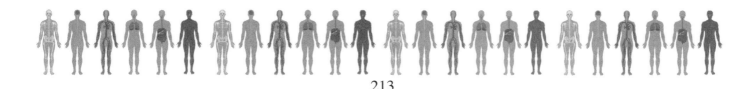

Answers to the Vocabulary Activities

VOCABULARY LIFT THE FLAP ANSWERS
LESSON 1

ANATOMY

The study of the human body, all its parts, and how it's put together.

HYPOTHESIS

An educated guess.

CELL MEMBRANE

The wall around a cell.

NUCLEUS

The control center of the cell.

PHYSIOLOGY

The study of how all the parts of the body function.

CYTOPLASM

The jelly-like substance inside a cell, in which all the organelles float.

LYSOSOMES

Organelles that protect the cell from foreign invaders and break down chemicals.

MITOCHONDRIA

The organelles inside the cell that give the cell power.

Anatomy Identification Answers
Lesson 2

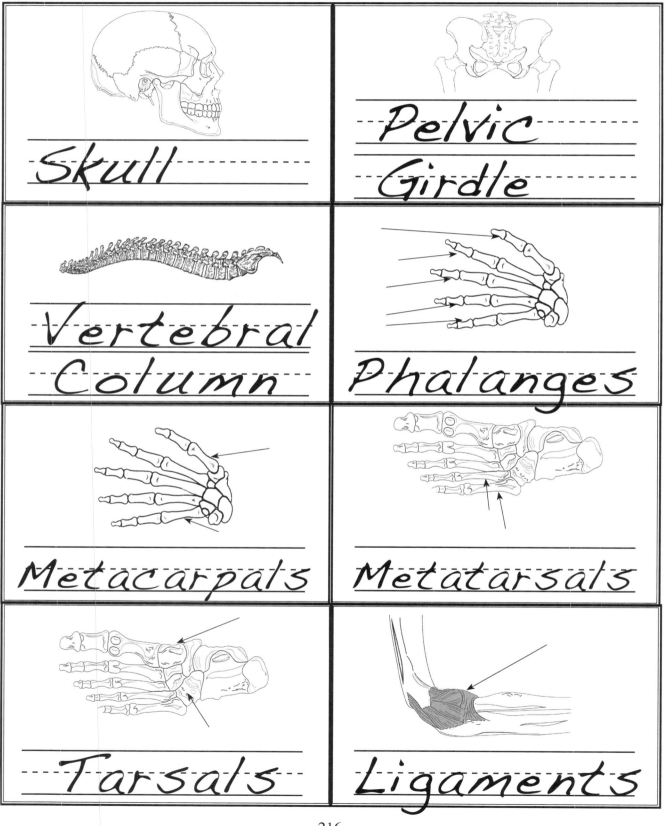

Skull

Pelvic Girdle

Vertebral Column

Phalanges

Metacarpals

Metatarsals

Tarsals

Ligaments

Vocabulary Puzzle Game
Answers Lesson 3

Voluntary Muscles

This is another name for skeletal muscles, because you can control them by thinking about controlling them.

Antagonistic Muscles

A pair of muscle groups that pulls the bone in opposite directions.

Tendons

These connect skeletal muscles to the bones.

Atrophy

A condition that occurs when a muscle is under-used and therefore becomes weak and shrinks.

Skeletal Muscles

The muscles that are attached to your bones.

Smooth Muscles

These muscles do not have stripes (striations) and are found in blood vessels, the stomach, the intestines and the bladder.

DIGESTION CROSSWORD ANSWERS

```
                    ¹M              ²E
                     E               P           ³L
                     C               I            A
                     H               G            R              ⁴A
                     A               L            G               L
                     N               O            G         ⁶D E N T I N
                  ⁵E  I               T            I               M
                   N  C               T            N               E
                   A  A               S                            N
       ⁷C H E M I C A L D I G E S T I O N                          T
                   E  L                        E                   A
                ⁸E  E                          S                   R
                 N  L                          T                   Y
                 Z      ⁹K I D N E Y S         I                   C
                 Y                             N                   A
       ¹⁰S M A L L I N T E S T I N E           E                   N
                 E                                                 A
                 S              I                                  L
                                O
                                N
```

VOCABULARY LIFT THE FLAP ANSWERS LESSON 5

CARBOHYDRATES

Carbon, hydrogen and oxygen atoms that are linked together and broken down to give your body the energy it needs.

VITAMIN DEFICIENCY

A condition or disease that occurs when your body doesn't get the proper amount of a vitamin it needs.

NUTRIENTS

Substances found in foods and drinks that your body needs to be healthy.

ESSENTIAL FATTY ACIDS

Fatty acids that you need that your body can't make.

ATOMS

The very smallest particles of an element. Everything you see is made from atoms.

PROTEINS

Strands of amino acids that are found in every cell in your body that help to keep your body running smoothly.

CALORIES

Units we use to measure energy.

MOLECULES

Two or more different kinds of atoms linked together.

Anatomy Identification Answers
Lesson 6

ALVEOLI	BRONCHI
NASAL CAVITY	TRACHEA
DIAPHRAGM	LARYNX

Vocabulary Puzzle Game
Answers Lesson 7

Leukocytes

Another name for white blood cells.

Circulatory System

The system that carries your blood throughout your body.

Phagocytes

Special white blood cells that eat dangerous or worn-out cells.

Anemia

A condition that is commonly the result of not having enough iron in the body.

Hemoglobin

The special oxygen carrying protein that red blood cells make and use. It also gives the red blood cells their red color.

Erythrocytes

Another name for red blood cells.

VOCABULARY LIFT THE FLAP ANSWERS
LESSON 8

ATRIUM

One of the top chambers of the heart.

VENTRICLES

The two lower chambers of the heart. These muscular chambers push the blood around your body.

PULMONARY VEINS

Veins that carry oxygenated blood from the lungs to the heart.

BLOOD PRESSURE

A measurement of the force of the blood pushing against the walls of the arteries.

AORTA

The largest artery in the body. It carries oxygenated blood away from the heart to arteries serving the body.

INFERIOR VENA CAVA

The large vein that collects blood from the lower parts of the body.

SUPERIOR VENA CAVA

The large vein that collects blood from the upper parts of the body.

PULMONARY ARTERIES

The only arteries that carry deoxygenated blood (blood that has a lower level of oxygen in it). They carry blood from the right ventricle to the lungs.

Nervous System Hangers
Lesson 9

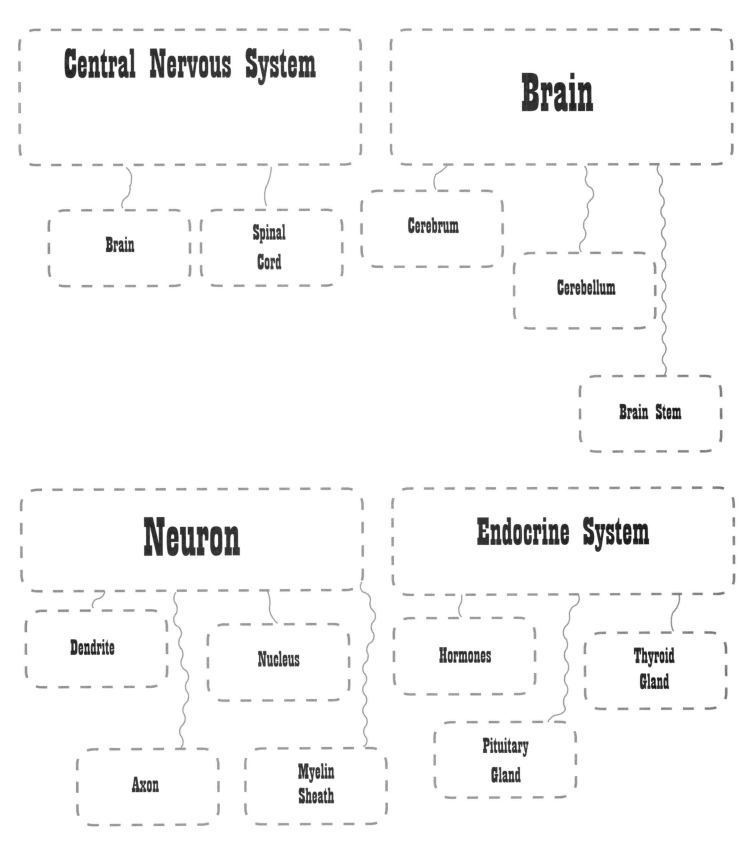

Central Nervous System

Brain

Brain

Spinal Cord

Cerebrum

Cerebellum

Brain Stem

Neuron

Endocrine System

Dendrite

Nucleus

Hormones

Thyroid Gland

Axon

Myelin Sheath

Pituitary Gland

Anatomy Identification Lesson 10

FRONTAL LOBE

PARIETAL LOBE

OCCIPITAL LOBE

TEMPORAL LOBE

SPINAL CORD

NERVES

ANATOMY MATCH UP ANSWERS LESSON 11

Smelling

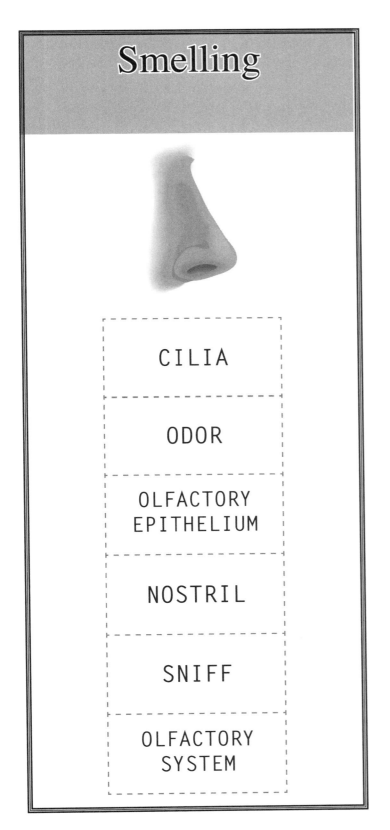

CILIA

ODOR

OLFACTORY EPITHELIUM

NOSTRIL

SNIFF

OLFACTORY SYSTEM

Tasting

PAPILLAE

SALTY

TASTE BUDS

SALIVA

SOUR

SWEET

ANATOMY MATCH UP
ANSWERS LESSON 11

Hearing Balancing

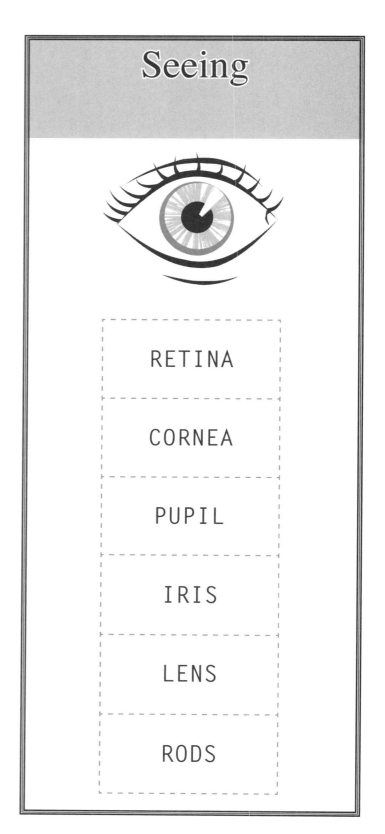

- VESTIBULE
- MACULA
- EARDRUM
- OTOLITHS
- SEMICIRCULAR CANALS
- PINNA

Seeing

- RETINA
- CORNEA
- PUPIL
- IRIS
- LENS
- RODS

VOCABULARY LIFT THE FLAP ANSWERS
LESSON 12

LUNULA

The half-moon shaped area of paleness beyond the cuticle of your nail. It is part of the nail matrix.

CLEAVAGE LINES

Patterns of indentions in your skin.

EPIDERMIS

The outer layer of your skin.

MELANIN

Lots of this pigment will make skin brown, olive or black.

SEBACEOUS GLANDS

Oil glands that are like built-in skin lotion dispensers.

HAIR FOLLICLE

A little "pocket" from which hair grows.

DERMIS

The inner layer of your skin.

INTEGUMENTARY SYSTEM

Your skin (along with your nails, hair, sweat glands, and oil glands) makes up this complex group of tissues.

Vocabulary Puzzle Game
Answers Lesson 13

Immunity

A system of defense against pathogens and cancers.

Lymphatic System

The body's defense system that includes 500 small, bean-shaped filters located throughout the body. They produce white blood cells called lymphocytes that destroy invaders.

Spleen

The largest of the lymph organs. Its main job is to filter blood.

Pathogens

Microscopic germs that get inside your body and can potentially cause an infection.

Malignant

A disease that is life threatening.

Artificial Immunity

Immunity that we get from vaccinations.

GROWTH AND DEVELOPMENT CROSSWORD ANSWERS

	P	U	B	E	R	T	Y				

Across and down answers:

- 1. PUBERTY
- 2. RECESSIVE
- 3. MITOSIS
- 4. CHROMOSOME
- 5. HEREDITY
- 6. MEIOSIS / MEIOSGENE
- 7. GENE
- 8. EMBRYO
- 9. DOMINANT GENE
- 10. TRAIT / GENETIC
- 11. FETUS

CREATION CONFIRMATION MINI BOOK

(Instructions on back)

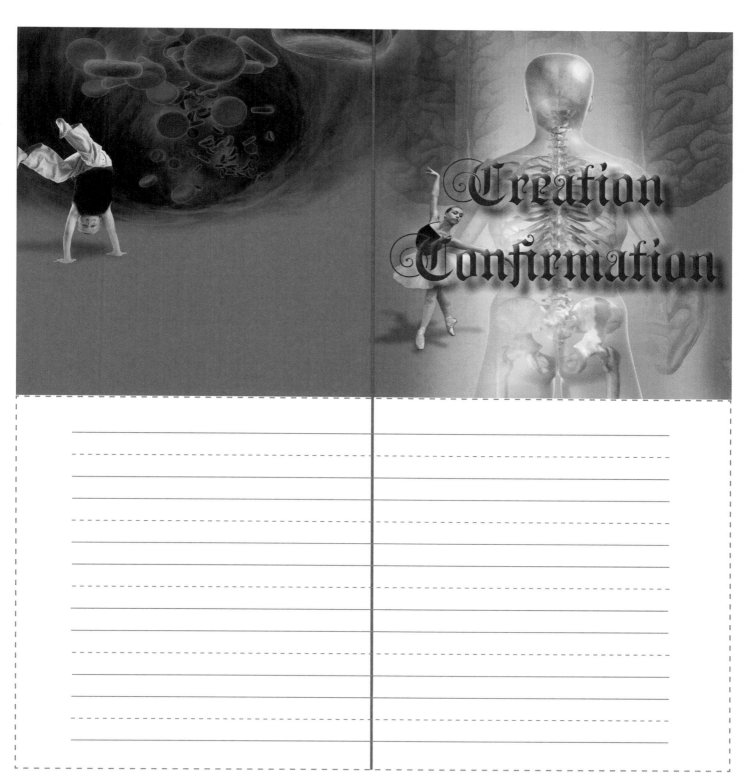

It's important to remember all you've learned about God and Creation in this course. This Creation Confirmation Book will enable you to record and recall your learning.

Instructions:
1. Cut out the Creation Confirmation Book rectangles on pages A1 and A3 along the dotted lines. **Do not cut the gold fold lines!**
2. Fold the pages along the gold lines.
3. Place the pages inside the blue cover of the book.
4. Open the book to the middle and staple it along the center.
5. As you work through each lesson of the anatomy course, write down what you learn about God, the Bible and Creation.
6. Keep your Creation Confirmation Book inside your anatomy book as a bookmark and a reminder to write down the things you learn about God.

Creation Confirmation Miniature Book

Creation Confirmation Miniature Book

EXTRA MINIATURE BOOKS

Here are a few extra miniature books for you to use.

Cut out the miniature books, but do not cut the black fold lines! Record any additional information you've learned about anatomy not included in the other miniature books. Fold your books and glue the back covers of the books onto the paste page of the topic you have written about.

Glue this side of the book to your paste page.

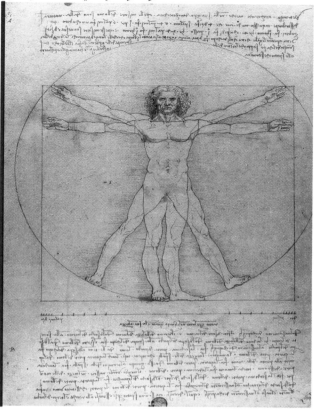

Glue this side of the book to your paste page.

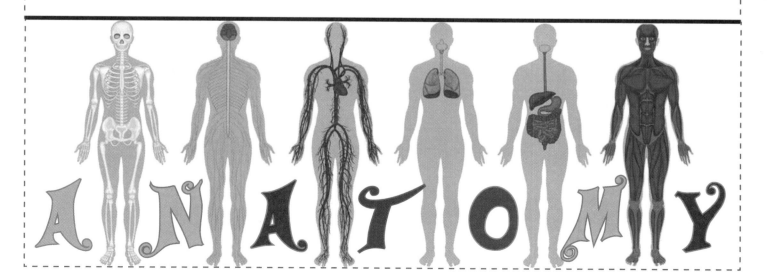

Instructions:

1. Cut out the Cell Circle and the Fact Circle. Be sure to cut out the white empty spaces in the Cell Circle.
2. Place the Cell Circle on top of the Fact Circle, and insert a brass fastener in the center (on the gold spot) to secure the two circles.
3. On the triangle opposite each title, write what that organelle does or draw a picture of it.
4. Dab glue on the bottom of the Fact Circle and glue your Cell Wheel onto the "Cell Minibook" paste page *(NJ p. 26)*.
5. Turn the Cell Circle around to reveal the different facts about each topic.

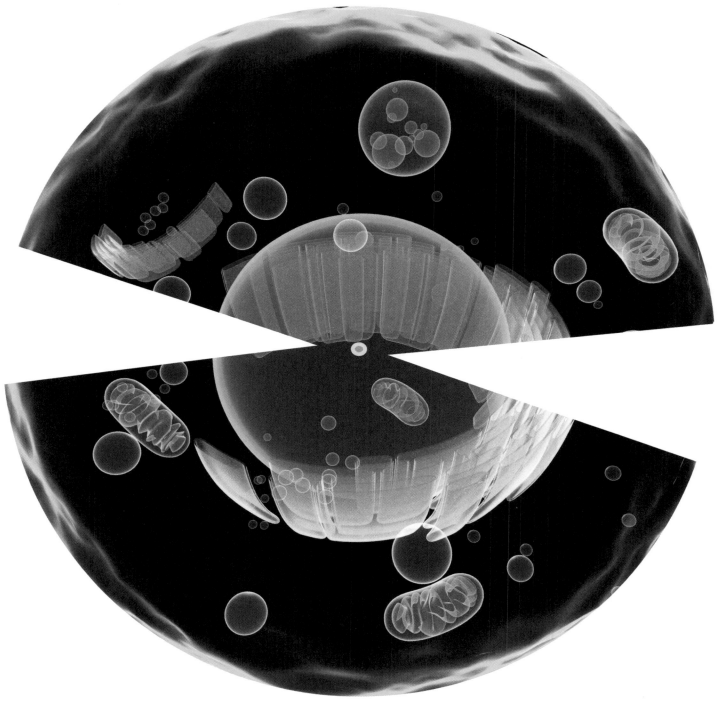

Cell Circle

Fact Circle

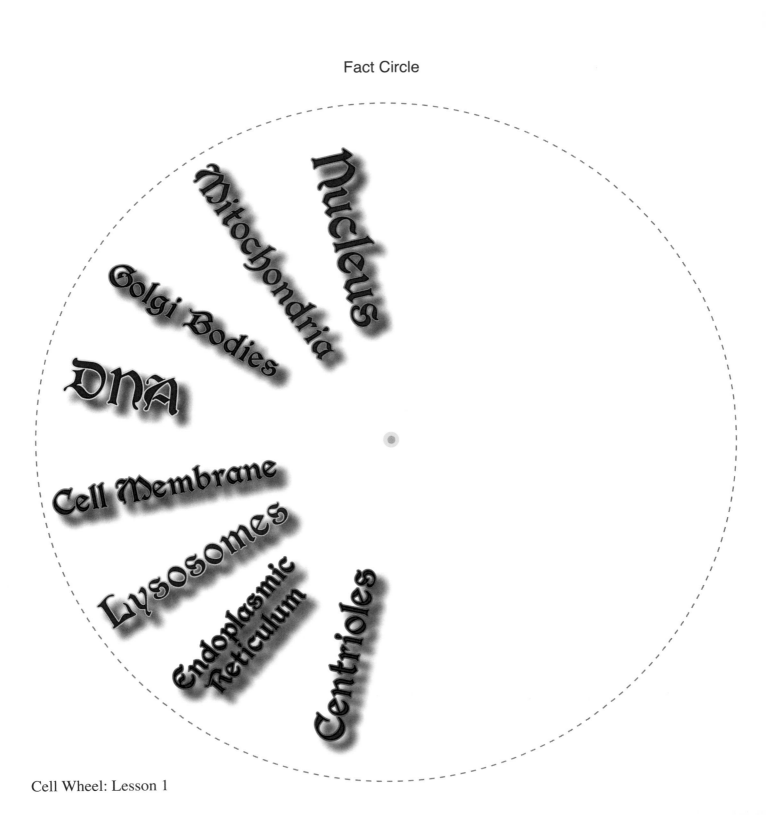

Nucleus

Mitochondria

Golgi Bodies

DNA

Cell Membrane

Lysosomes

Endoplasmic Reticulum

Centrioles

Cell Wheel: Lesson 1

Glue this side to your paste page.

SKELETAL SYSTEM SHUTTER BOOK

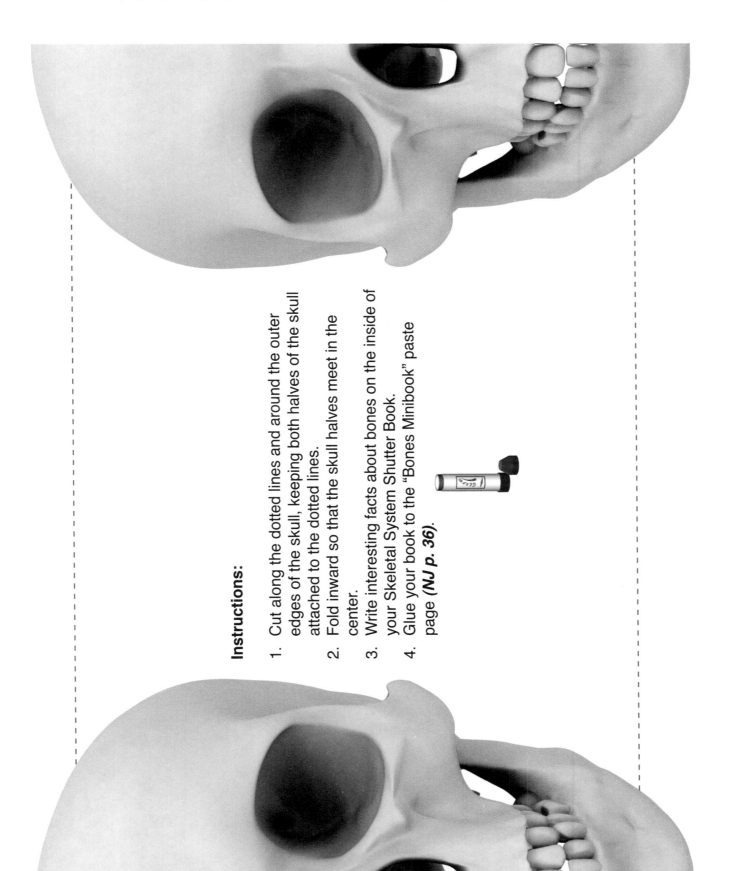

Instructions:

1. Cut along the dotted lines and around the outer edges of the skull, keeping both halves of the skull attached to the dotted lines.

2. Fold inward so that the skull halves meet in the center.

3. Write interesting facts about bones on the inside of your Skeletal System Shutter Book.

4. Glue your book to the "Bones Minibook" paste page *(NJ p. 36)*.

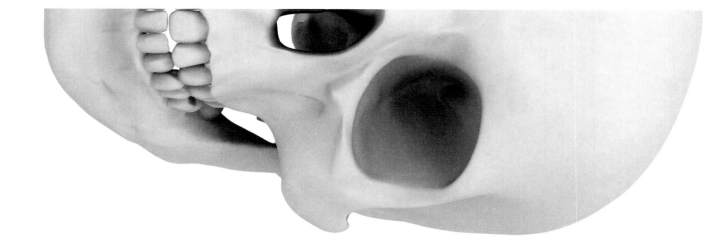

BONES

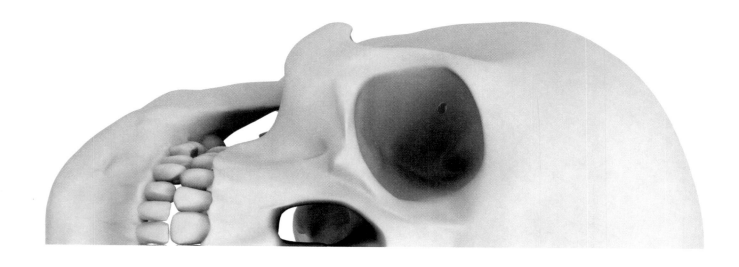

MUSCULAR SYSTEM FLAP BOOK

What are Tendons?

What are Skeletal Muscles?

Describe Muscle Cells.

Why is Protein Important?

How do Muscles Grow?

Instructions:

1. Cut out the large rectangle on this page along the dotted lines.
2. Cut between the colored rectangles along the four dotted lines that divide the rectangles. **Do not cut into the orange fold lines!**
3. Fold the colored rectangles away from you along the orange fold lines.
4. Turn over your Muscular System Flap Book and lift the flaps.
5. Write the information requested about the topics on the flaps.
6. Glue this side (with these words) to your "Muscles Minibook" paste page *(NJ p. 52)*.

What is Cardiac Muscle?

More Muscle Facts

Muscular System Flap Book: Lesson 3

DIGESTION POCKET

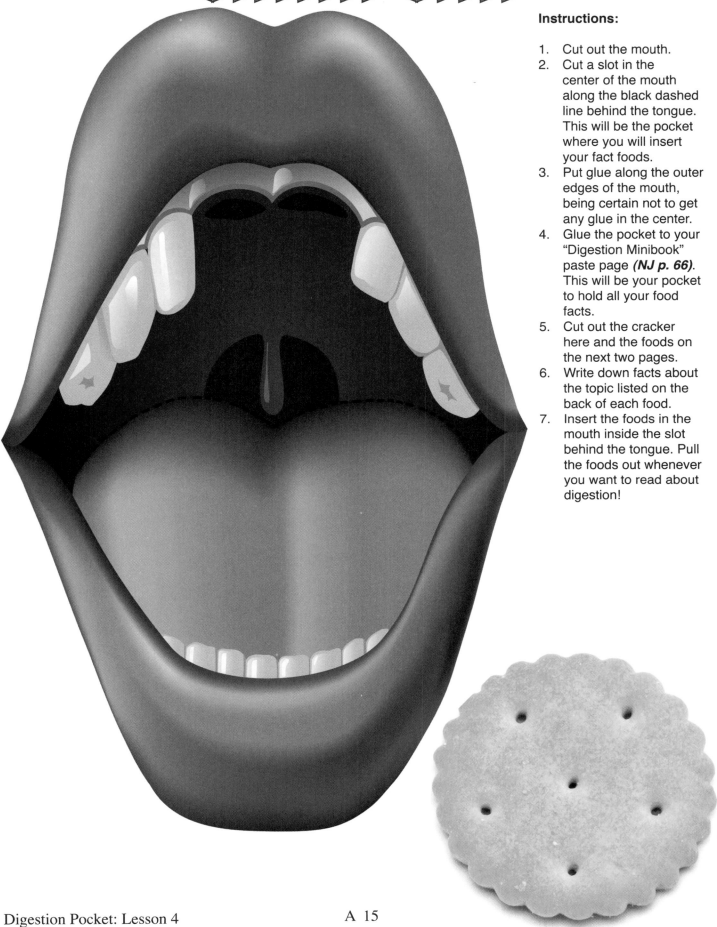

Instructions:

1. Cut out the mouth.
2. Cut a slot in the center of the mouth along the black dashed line behind the tongue. This will be the pocket where you will insert your fact foods.
3. Put glue along the outer edges of the mouth, being certain not to get any glue in the center.
4. Glue the pocket to your "Digestion Minibook" paste page *(NJ p. 66)*. This will be your pocket to hold all your food facts.
5. Cut out the cracker here and the foods on the next two pages.
6. Write down facts about the topic listed on the back of each food.
7. Insert the foods in the mouth inside the slot behind the tongue. Pull the foods out whenever you want to read about digestion!

Saliva Facts

Tooth Diagram

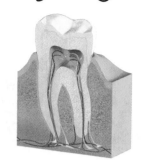

Label the Teeth

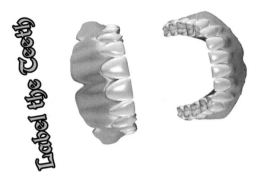

Intestine Facts

ALIMENTARY CANAL

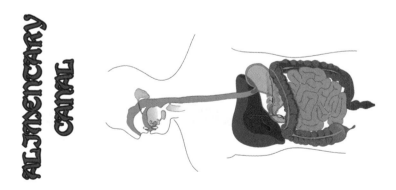

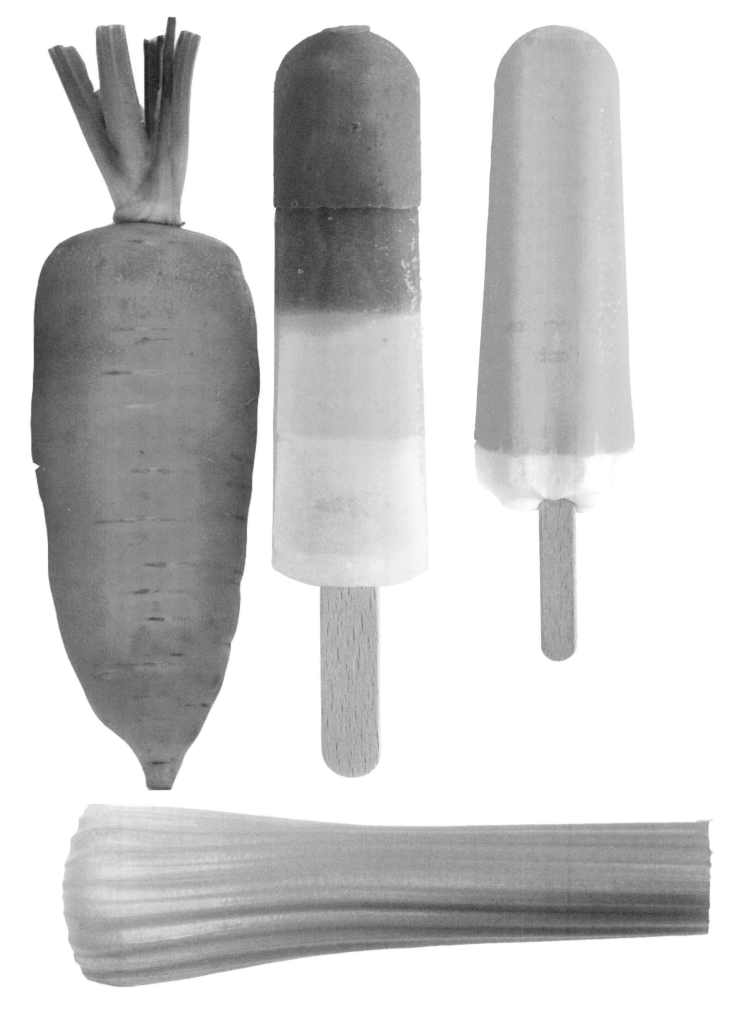

Liver
Facts

Mechanical
Digestion

Chemical
Digestion

Digestion
Facts

Pancreas
Facts

Bolus

Chyme

Stomach Facts

This is the matchbook cover that will hold all your rectangular pages.

Instructions:

1. Cut out this matchbook cover. **Do not cut the blue fold lines!**
2. Fold along the blue lines so that the large foods flap and the small cherries flap face outward in the same direction.
3. Cut out the rectangles on this page and the next and fill in the information you learned about each topic.
4. Lift the large flap and place all the pages you created under the small flap.
5. With the large cover flap open and your pages under the small flap, staple your matchbook on the white line that crosses the center of the small flap. This will hold all your pages inside. **Do not staple the cover closed!**
6. Fold the large flap down and tuck it into the small flap, like a matchbook.
7. Glue this side (with these words) onto the "Nutrition Minibook" paste page *(NJ p. 82)*.

Protein

Carbohydrates

Calcium

Water

Nutrition Matchbook: Lesson 5

Vitamin C

_____
- - - - - - - - -
_____
- - - - - - - - -
_____
- - - - - - - - -
_____

Fats

_____
- - - - - - - - -
_____
- - - - - - - - -
_____
- - - - - - - - -
_____

RESPIRATORY MINI BOOKS

Instructions:

1. Cut out the Respiratory Mini Books along the dotted lines. **Do not cut the yellow fold lines!**
2. Fold the books along the yellow lines so the images are on the outside of the books.
3. Write facts you learned about the parts of the respiratory system listed on each book.
4. Glue your mini books onto the "Respiratory Minibooks" paste page *(NJ p. 94)*.

Glue this side of the book to your paste page.

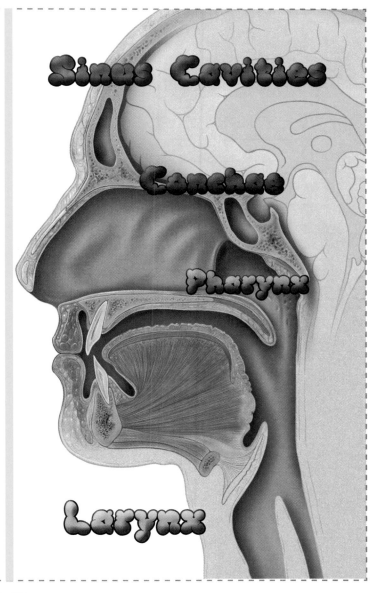

Sinus Cavities

Conchae

Pharynx

Larynx

Respiratory Mini Books: Lesson 6

Glue this side of the book to your paste page.

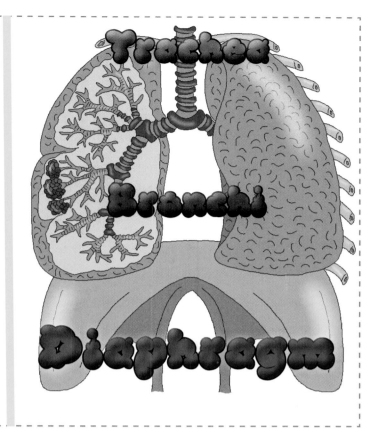

Glue this side of the book to your paste page.

Trachea

- -

Bronchi

- -

Diaphragm

- -

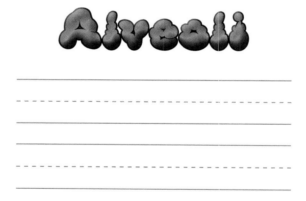

Alveoli

- -

- -

BLOOD SHUTTER BOOKS

Instructions:

1. Cut out the four Blood Shutter Books on this page and the next. **Do not cut the gold fold lines!**
2. Fold the flaps of the books inward along the gold fold lines.
3. Open the flaps and write what you learned about blood on the insides of the books.
4. Glue your Blood Shutter Books onto the "Blood Minibooks" paste page *(NJ p. 108)*.

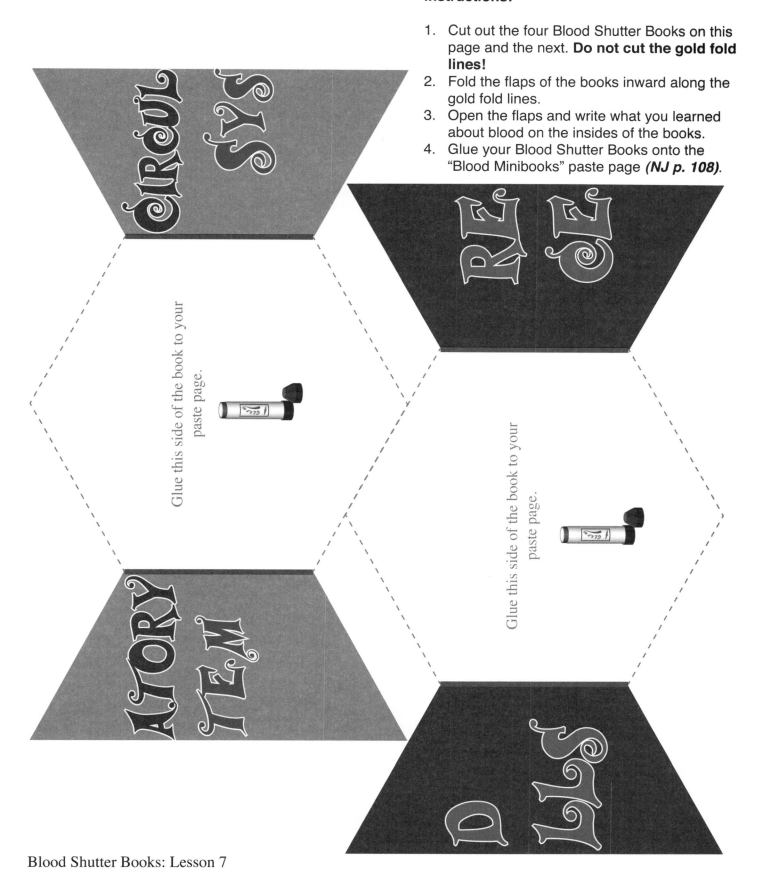

Blood Shutter Books: Lesson 7

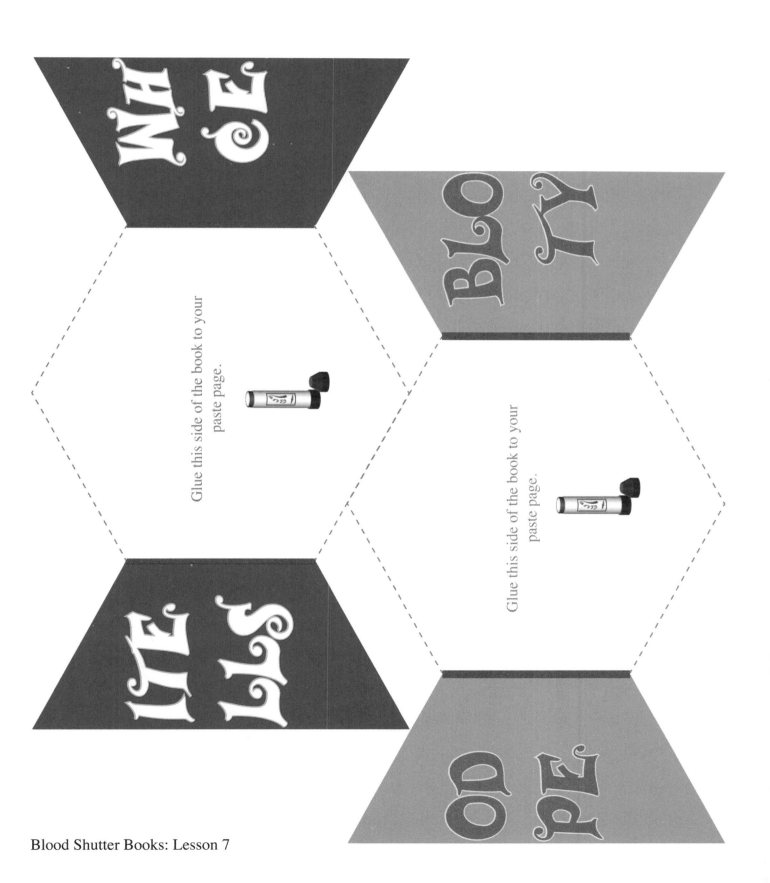

Glue this side of the book to your paste page.

Glue this side of the book to your paste page.

CARDIO TUCK IN ENVELOPES

Instructions:

1. Cut out each Tuck In Envelope along the dotted lines. **Do not cut the red fold lines!**

2. Fold the books inward along the red fold lines to resemble an envelope.

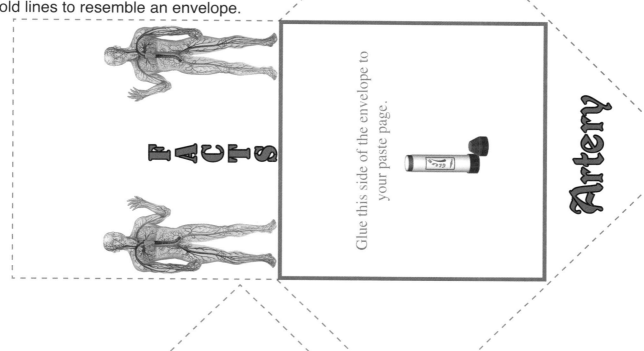

FACTS

Glue this side of the envelope to your paste page.

Artery

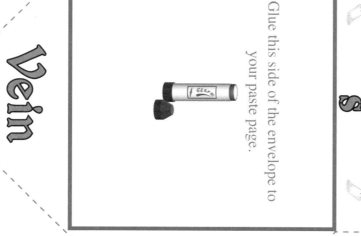

Vein

Glue this side of the envelope to your paste page.

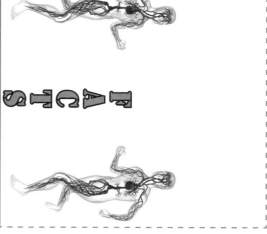

FACTS

3. On the inside of each envelope, write what you learned about the topic listed on the outside of the envelope.

4. Glue your envelopes onto the "Cardiovascular Minibooks" paste page **(NJ p. 120)**.

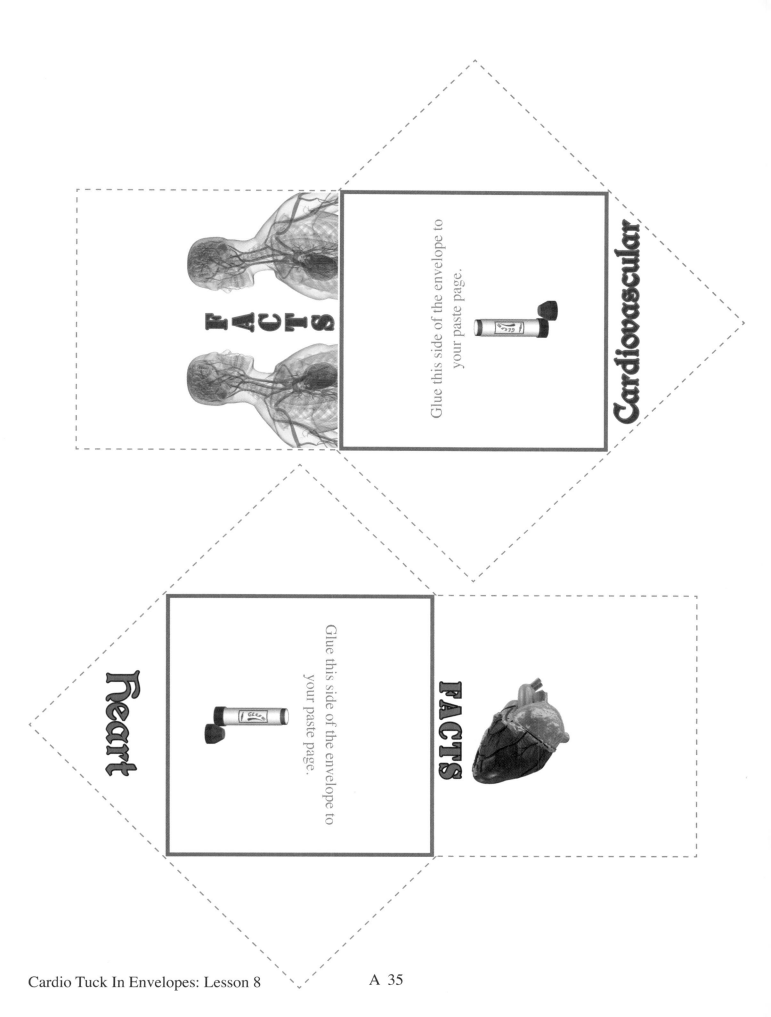

Glue this side of the envelope to your paste page.

Cardiovascular

FACTS

Heart

Glue this side of the envelope to your paste page.

FACTS

Cardio Tuck In Envelopes: Lesson 8

NERVOUS SYSTEM LAYERED BOOK

Instructions:

1. Write down facts you learned under each title listed on the rectangle pages of your layered book.
2. Cut out the four pages and the title page along the dotted lines.
3. Stack the pages on top of each other with the smallest title page on top.
4. Line the pages up at the top with the title of each page showing at the bottom.
5. Staple the pages along the top to secure them together.
6. Glue your layered book onto the "Nervous System Minibook" paste page *(NJ p. 138)*.
7. Lift the layers to read about the nervous system.

CENTRAL NERVOUS SYSTEM

CNS

PERIPHERAL NERVOUS SYSTEM

PNS

Nervous System Layered Book: Lesson 9

NERVOUS SYSTEM

AUTONOMIC NERVOUS SYSTEM

_____

_____

_____

_____

SOMATIC NERVOUS SYSTEM

_____

_____

_____

_____

_____

ANS - SNS

DRAW AND LABEL A NEURON

NEURONS

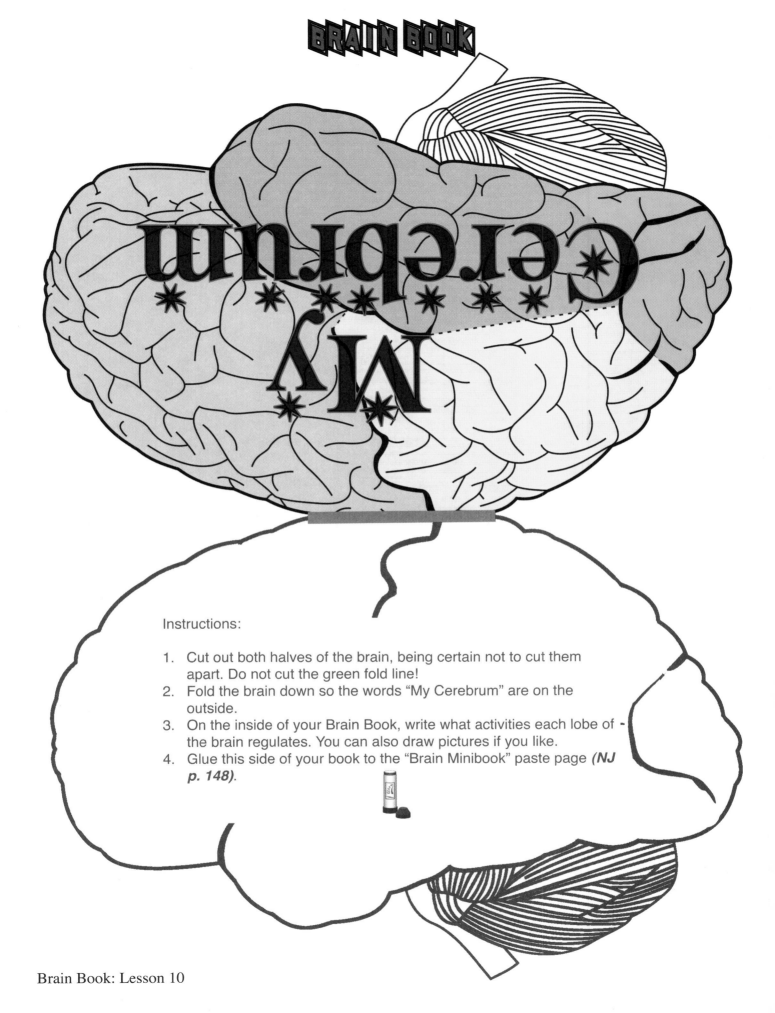

BRAIN BOOK

My Cerebrum

Instructions:

1. Cut out both halves of the brain, being certain not to cut them apart. Do not cut the green fold line!
2. Fold the brain down so the words "My Cerebrum" are on the outside.
3. On the inside of your Brain Book, write what activities each lobe of the brain regulates. You can also draw pictures if you like.
4. Glue this side of your book to the "Brain Minibook" paste page *(NJ p. 148)*.

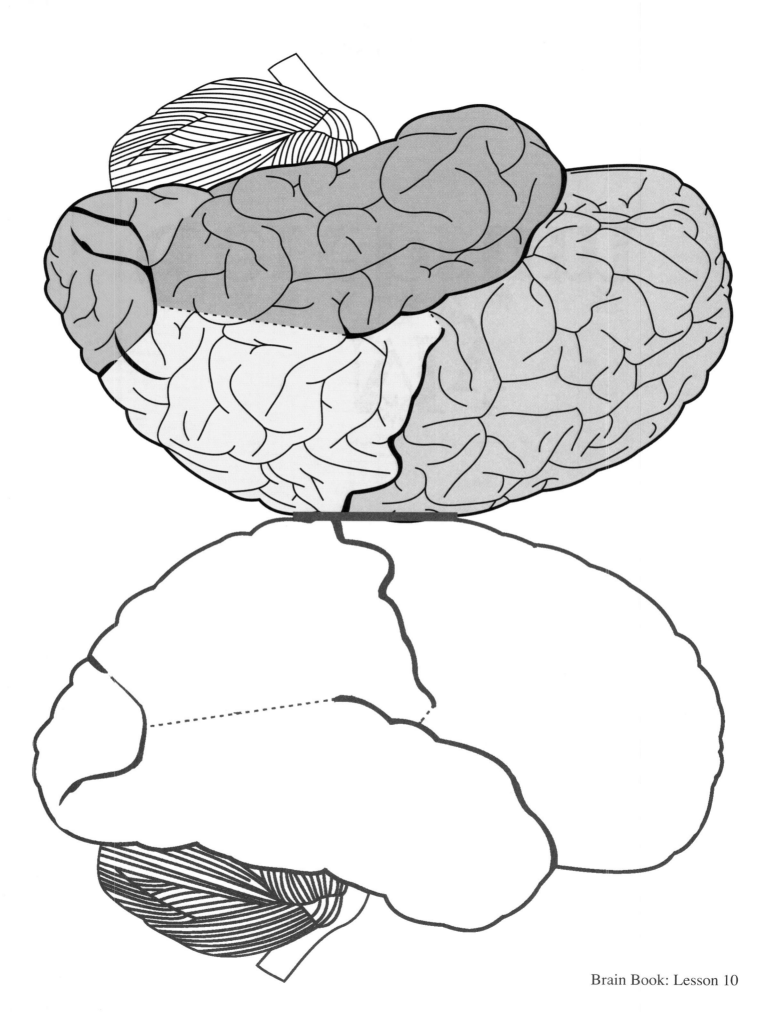

Instructions:

1. Cut out the tabbed rectangles on this and the next two pages. Fold the green cover page along the yellow fold line.
2. Fold the smell and balance page along the yellow fold line so the word "smell" is on the outside when folded. Place this page inside the green cover page.
3. Fold the taste and hearing page along the yellow line so the word "taste" is on the outside. Place the page in the center of the book so the tabs line up down the side of the book when it is closed.
4. Open the book and staple it down the center by inserting a stapler across half the book.
5. Write or draw what you learned about your senses on the pages of your book. Be sure to label the diagrams.
6. Glue your Five Senses Tab Book onto your "Senses Minibook" paste page *(NJ p. 163)*.

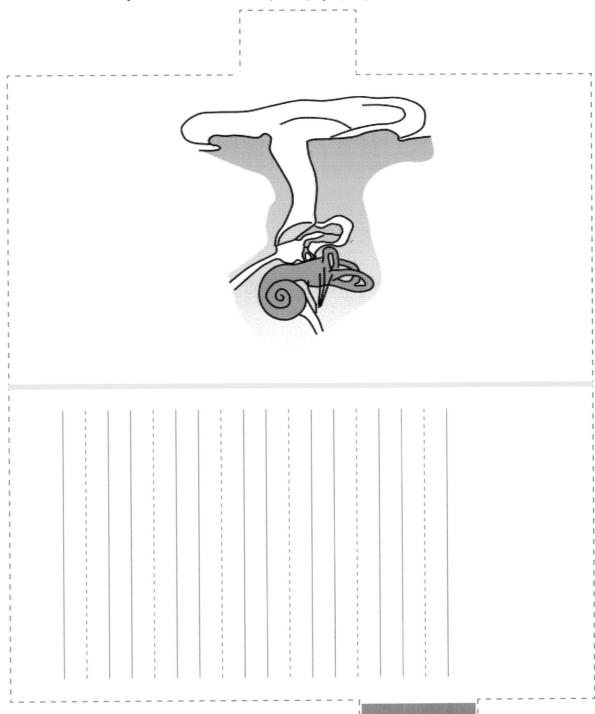

Five Senses Tab Book: Lesson 11   A 43

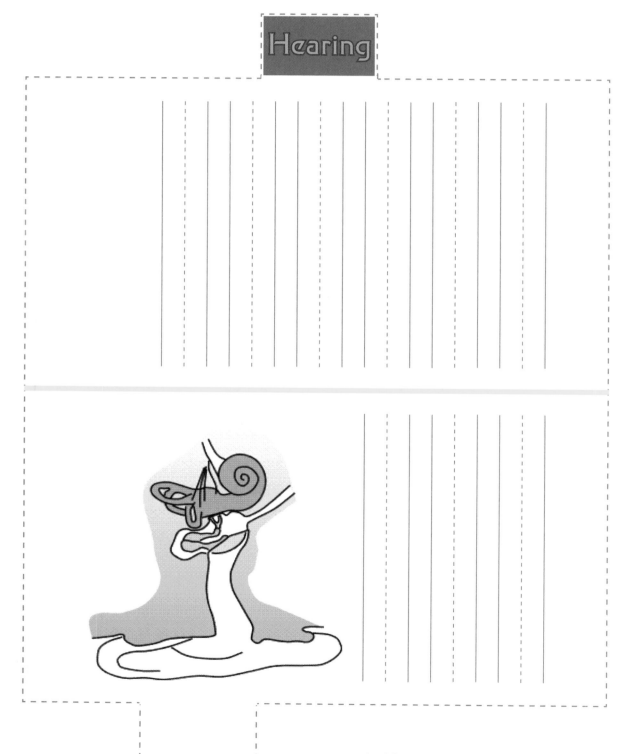

Hearing

A 44

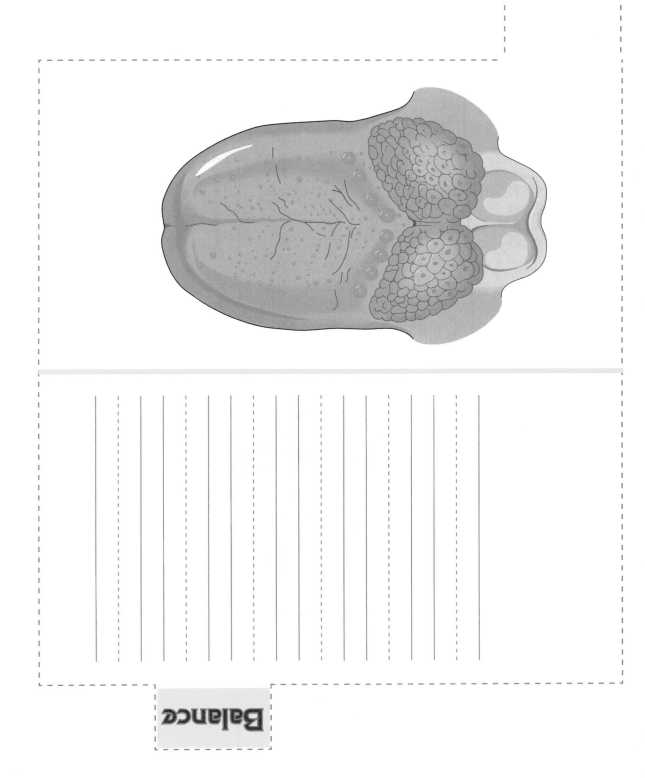

Balance

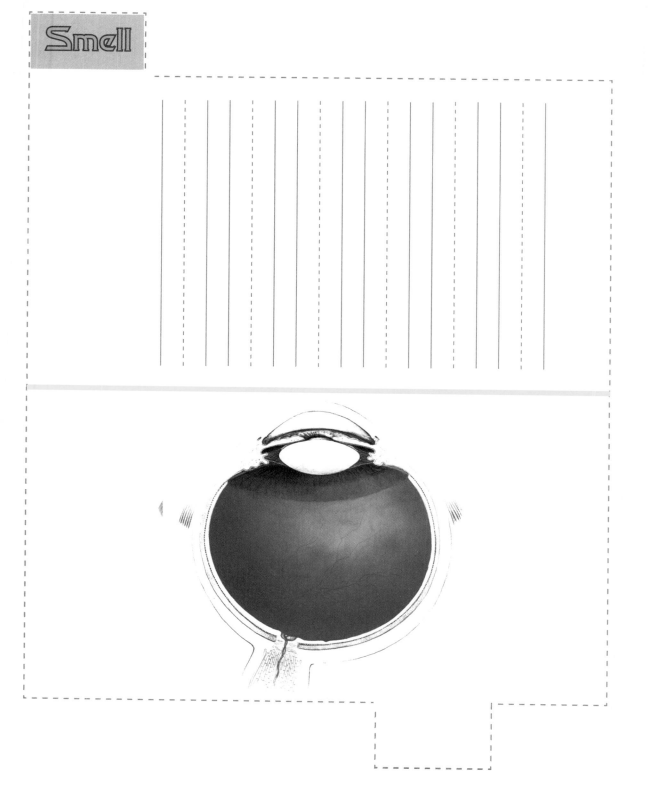

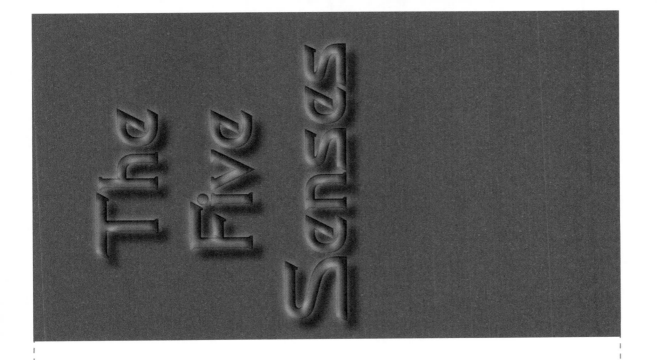

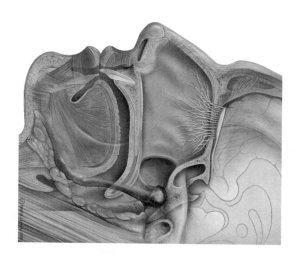

Sight

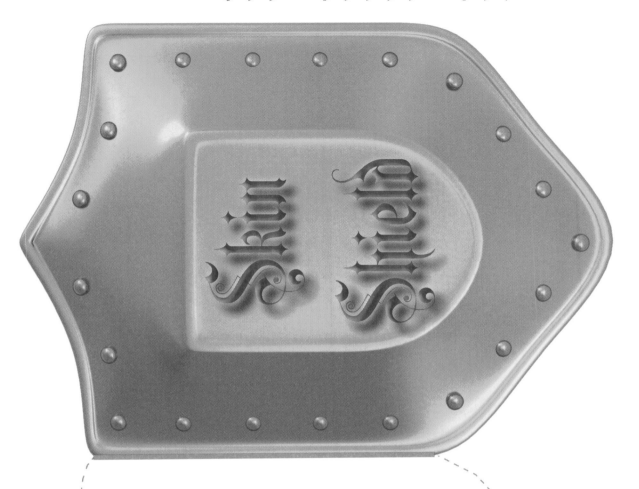

Instructions:

1. Cut out this shield book cover and the book pages along the dotted lines. Do not cut the blue fold lines!
2. Fold the cover and pages, inserting the pages inside the cover of the book.
3. Open the book flat. Using a stapler, reach into the center of the book and staple along the fold line to secure the pages to the cover page of the book.
4. Write information you learned about the integumentary system on the pages.
5. Glue your Skin Shield Book onto your "Integumentary Minibook" paste page (*NJ p. 178)*.

Integumentary Shield Book: Lesson 12

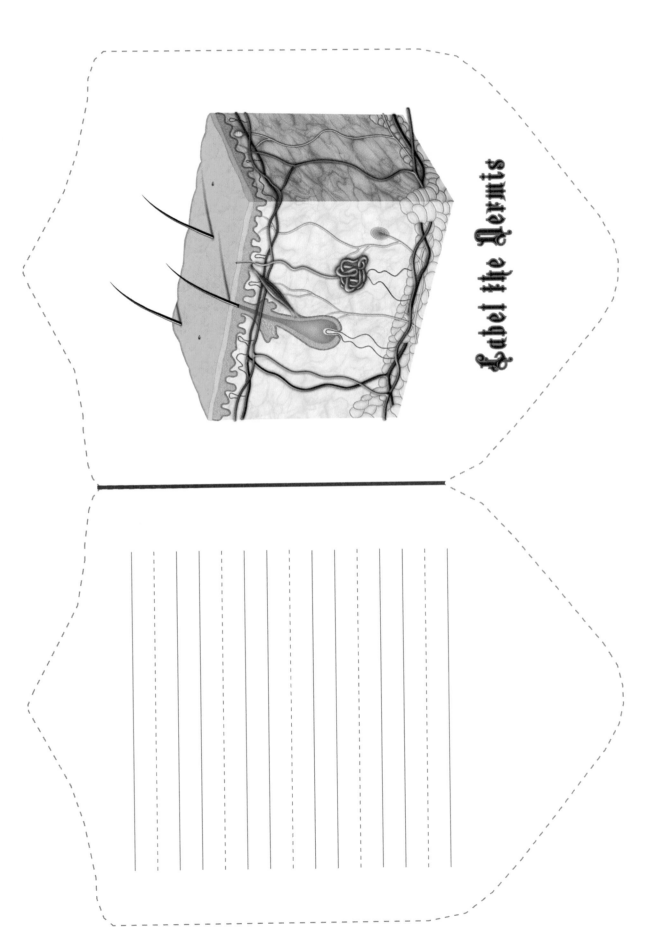

Label the Dermis

DEFENSE ACCORDION BOOK

Instructions:

1. Cut out the two halves of the Defense Accordion Book, being sure to keep the top and bottom parts of the knight attached to the paper strips. The bottom half is on the backside of this page. **Be sure not to cut the blue fold lines!**
2. Glue the bottom half of the knight to the top half by putting glue on the glue tab and affixing it to the back of the immunity box.
3. Write what you learned about our amazing defense system under the topics listed on the paper strip.
4. Fold the long strip accordion style along the blue fold lines.
5. Glue the back of the knight's shoulders onto the "Defense Mini-book" paste page *(NJ p. 194)*.

BAD GUYS

LYMPHATIC SYSTEM

IMMUNITY

Glue this tab to the back of the "Immunity" box

B & T LYMPHOCYTES

ANTIBODIES

ANTIBIOTICS

GROWTH AND DEVELOPMENT FAN

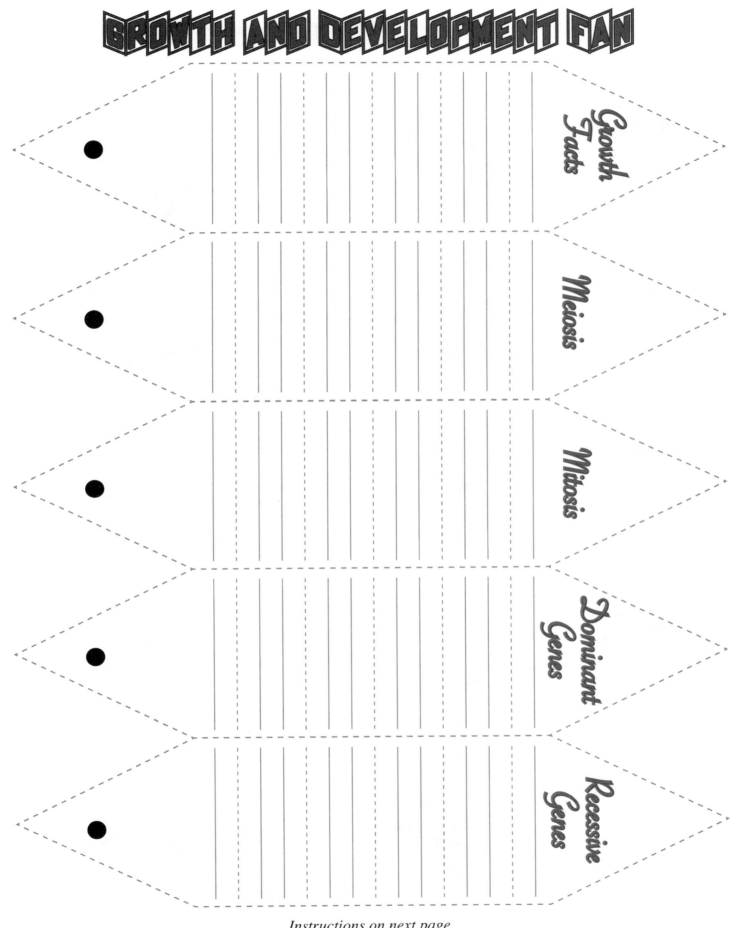

Growth Facts

Meiosis

Mitosis

Dominant Genes

Recessive Genes

Instructions on next page

Growth and Development Fan: Lesson 14   A 55

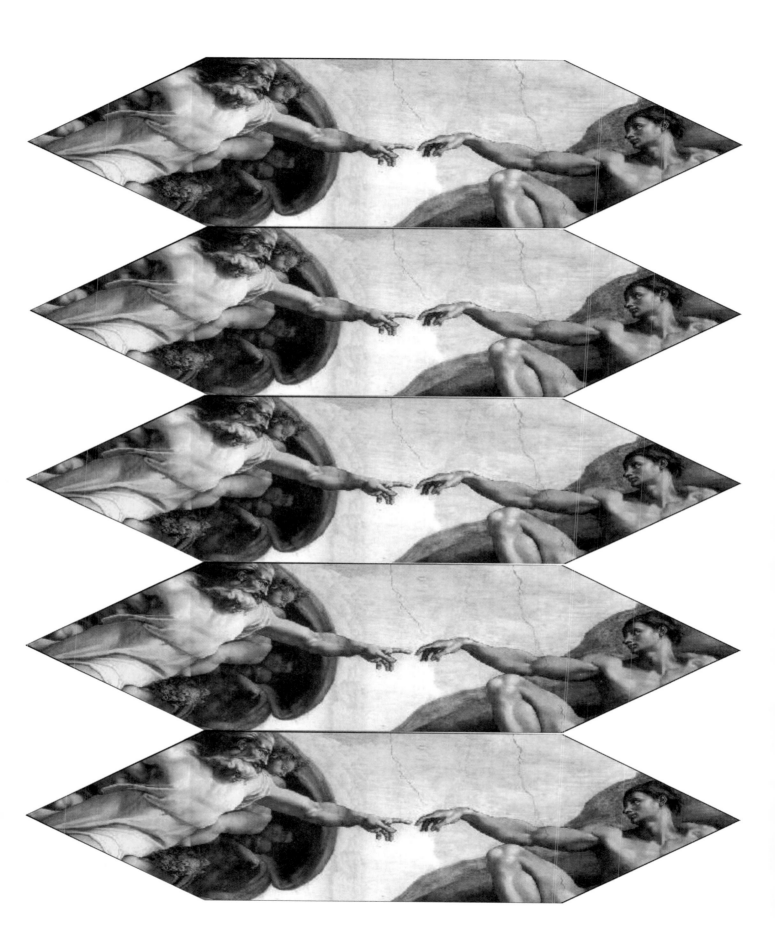

A 56   Growth and Development Fan: Lesson 14

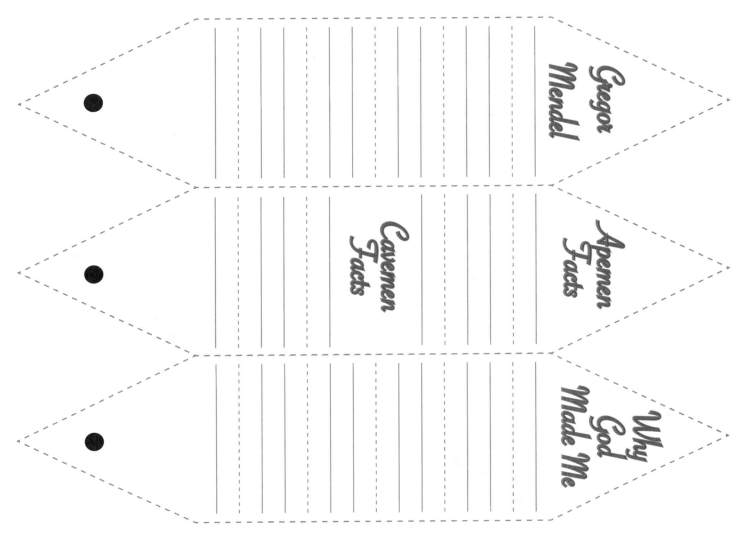

Gregor Mendel

Apemen Facts

Cavemen Facts

Why God Made Me

Growth and Development Pocket

Instructions:

1. Cut out each individual fan sheet (on this page and the previous).
2. Punch a hole in the bottom of each fan sheet on the black dot.
3. Fill in the information requested under each topic.
4. Stack your fan sheets with the Creation of Adam image sheet on top.
5. Secure the fan sheets at the bottom by inserting a brass fastener into the punch hole.
6. Cut out the pocket to the left.
7. Put glue on the bottom and side edges and paste the pocket onto your "Growth and Development" paste page *(NJ p. 208)*.
8. Place your Fan in the pocket and remove it when you want to read all about Growth and Development.

Growth and Development Fan: Lesson 14

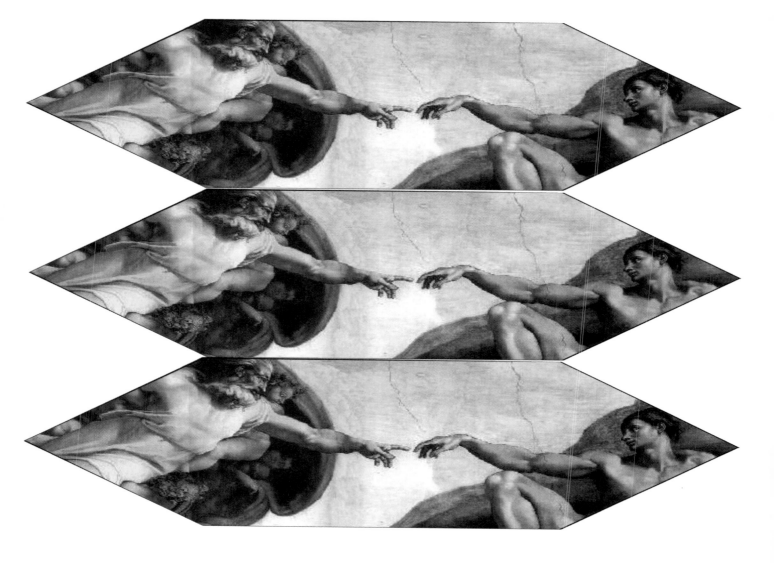

PERSONAL PERSON PROJECT

This section contains templates and illustrations for creating your Personal Person. Begin by choosing your body outline from the three colors offered here and on the next two pages. Next, add a photograph of your head to the top of the body. There are two body outlines for each color. The first outline will be placed on your Personal Person paste page (p. 13). The second will be used in Lesson 12, after you study the integumentary system. As you work through each of the lessons, carefully cut out the organ or body system on the pages that follow.

Personal Person Body Outline (Lesson 1)

Integumentary (skin) System (Lesson 12)

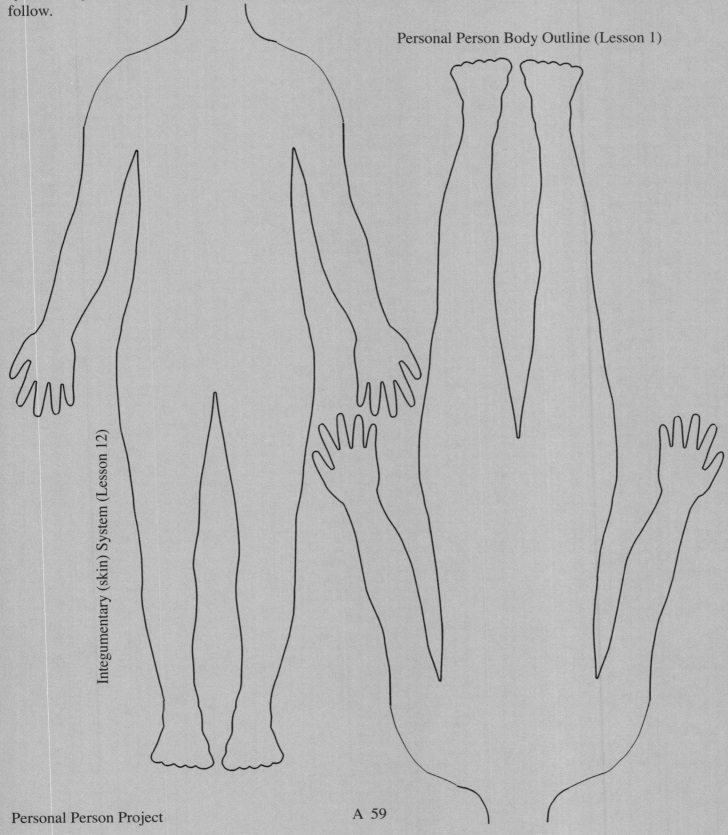